THE EVOLUTION OF THE GEAR ART

by

Darle W. Dudley
Chief of Gear Technology

Solar Division of International Harvester Company
San Diego, California

Published by:

American Gear Manufacturers Association
Washington, D.C.

1969

Copyright © 1969

American Gear Manufacturers Association
1330 Massachusetts Avenue, N. W.
Washington, D. C. 20005

Library of Congress Catalog
Card Number: 72-78509

Printed in the United States of America
by Frank Gordon Printing Company
Washington, D.C.

Dedicated to

Dorothy Winslow Dudley – my wife

FOREWORD

The Administrative Family and members of the American Gear Manufacturers Association are happy and proud to help in bringing this authoritative work by Mr. Darle W. Dudley to your attention.

Even a casual reading discloses that this is a genuine labor of love, coupled with a remarkable knowledge of our industry. A more thorough study will enrich the student, engineer, gear manufacturer, or gear user by giving each an insight into the manner in which gears have been and are being utilized to soften man's bumpy traverse of land, sea, and space.

No one but Mr. Dudley could have authored this book, because we know of no one so uniquely experienced in the ramifications of the gear field. Substantial evidence of this conclusion was shown in 1958 when the AGMA Awards Committee and Board of Directors named Mr. Dudley as recipient of the "Edward P. Connell Award", AGMA's highest annual honor that can be tendered to a gear oriented individual.

Washington, D.C.
October, 1968

John C. Sears
Executive Director
American Gear Manufacturers
Association

PREFACE

Anyone who has worked in the gear field for many years becomes impressed with the long, continued use of gears in all manner of machinery. Geared machines always seem to go right back to the beginning. The earliest automobiles, for instance, used gears. The early water mills, a few centuries ago used gears. The Romans, two milleniums ago, had geared devices. When, then, did the art of gearing start?

In recent years, I have tried to find out just how the gear art evolved. Many friends like Earle Buckingham, Gilbert Dannehower, Charles Staub, Russell Ball, Jr., Granger Davenport and Ted Miller have told me things they know about gear history and have suggested where I might search to find more information. The Smithsonian Institution in Washington, D.C. (and Edwin Battison of the Smithsonian) was very helpful. Books by Robert Woodbury, Sprague De Camp, Abbott Payson Usher and Ralph Flanders have provided excellent source material. Out of these sources and personal discussions with a great number of AGMA members, I have pieced together a story about how gears and the theory of gear engineering has developed.

The story that is told in this book is rather surprising. Gears have been around for at least 5,000 years! The gear art, born in the earliest times of antiquity, is growing (like so many other things) at an astonishing rate as we approach the end of the 20th century.

I am very pleased that the American Gear Manufacturers Association (AGMA) has been interested enough in this subject to sponsor the publication of, "The Evolution of The Gear Art".

My secretary, Mrs. M. Irene Galarneau, worked late at night to organize, edit and type my manuscript material for this book. I greatly appreciate her very capable assistance.

San Diego, California   Darle W. Dudley
October 6, 1968

TABLE OF CONTENTS

Chapter 1

INTRODUCTION TO GEARING AND ITS PLACE
IN THE ARTS AND CRAFTS OF MAN

The gearing industry of today is concerned not only with tooth gear wheels but with gear transmission packages involving casings, gears, shafts, bearings, clutches, couplings, lubrication systems and even the structure to support the gear plus its driving or driven device. All in all, gears and the things that go to make up gear packages are a very important part of the mechanical products manufactured in the United States. John Sears, the Executive Director of AGMA, has told me that their studies at AGMA Headquarters show an annual gear business of over one billion dollars in the United States. My own studies indicate that the total value of the gear transmissions in every device built – vehicle, machine, appliance, instrument, power system, tool, clock, implement, military weapon, electronics device, toy, gadget, etc. – may be closer to two billion dollars per year.

Gears are one of man's oldest mechanical devices. The toothed wheel takes its place with the lever, the inclined plane, the screw and the pulley as one of man's earliest devices to increase the force that could be applied to an object. The gear has been a basic element of machinery throughout all time from the earliest beginnings of machinery.

As a matter of fact, the candidates to be considered as the earliest machines of man would have to include the primitive gear train along with the primitive form of the potters' wheel, the primitive lathe and the ancient water-lifting devices.

Sentimentally, gears have always been associated in the popular mind with mechanical machinery. A "Rube Goldberg" cartoon of an invention will invariably depict gears in the device. Abbott Payson Usher's excellent book, "A History of Mechanical Inventions,"* chose some gear types as its cover illustration (see Fig. 1). Figure 2 shows the familiar gear wheel insignia of Rotary International that is a road-sign all over the United States. Figure 3 shows an example of the gear symbol used by the National Petroleum Institute on a brochure published in 1966. Numerous manufacturing companies – like National Cash Register – have chosen a gear to be part of the symbol of their company. The term "geared for progress" has symbolic meaning to anyone concerned with the mechanical arts.

In the public mind, gears are one of the most well recognized kinds of machinery. They create the impression of positive action, coordinated – interlocked – precise application of effort to secure a desired result.

*A selected bibliography is given at the end of the book.

The gear trade can be very proud of the fact that their craft is as old as civilization itself. For 5000 years gears have been used by man — and their use is ever increasing. Our newest supersonic airplanes will have hinged wings with gears used in the actuation system to move the wings. The supermarket of the future will deliver goods to a customer like a gigantic coin machine. Geared mechanisms will mechanically transfer the purchased articles from storage to the customer's car. Doctors will soon be implanting extremely tiny electro-mechanical devices in the human body to regulate body functions that a diseased organ can no longer properly control. Miniature gears of very high quality and miniature electronic components make this very humane work possible.

The gear industry has benefited greatly from the early establishment and forward looking development of a national trade association called the "American Gear Manufacturers Association" (AGMA). This history of the gear art was first presented at the AGMA Annual Convention at Hot Springs, Virginia, June 1966, as part of the program to commemorate the 50th anniversary of the founding of AGMA. The widespread interest in gears and gear history has led to the publication of this revised and enlarged work on the evolution of the gear art.

BEACON BP 84 $2.25

A History of
MECHANICAL
INVENTIONS

With a new
preface by
the author

Figure 1   Gears are used to illustrate the cover of Abbott Payson Usher's book. Courtesy of Beacon Press, Beacon Hill, Boston.

3

Figure 2   Rotary International uses the gear to indicate the sterling quality of the organization.

Partners in Defense

Figure 3   The symbol of interlocked gears indicates positive, coordinated action. Courtesy of National Petroleum Council, Washington, D.C.

Chapter 2

GEARING IN PRE–CHRISTIAN TIMES
3000 BC – 100 BC

Most writers trace gears back to the writings of Aristotle (around 330 BC). Aristotle writes of gears as if they were commonplace so the beginnings must go back much farther.

The earliest known relic of gearing from ancient times is the "South Pointing Chariot," circa 2600 BC. This chariot was not only geared but it contained a very complex differential gear train that is hard for even a modern gear engineer to analyze! A miniature replica of this chariot is on exhibit at the Smithsonian Institution at Washington, D.C.

The ancient Chinese apparently used this chariot to keep from getting lost while traveling through the Gobi Desert. It can be set so that the figure *points south and continues to point south regardless of which direction* the chariot is going.

The South Pointing Chariot used gearing made with wooden pins. These pins are clearly visible in Fig. 4. Figure 5 shows, in cartoon fashion, how this type of gear can be used on either a parallel axis or a right-angle axis drive.

In view of the intricacy of the South Pointing Chariot, it seems obvious that there must have been earlier use of gearing going back to at least 3000 BC. The earliest written records about gearing are dated from about 330 BC. This leaves a blank space of almost 3000 years during which gear devices must have been in use. Since there are no written records covering this interval, we must await the spade of the archaeologist to fill in our knowledge.

Writings of Philo of Byzantium and Hero of Alexandria indicate that prayer wheel devices in Egyptian temples were developed to the point where trains of gears were used. Apparently the worshipper could get blessed more thoroughly with the help of speed-increasing gears. De Camp[1] remarks that gears led to "more salvation per revolution."

From many writings it seems probable that both the Egyptians and Babylonians were using gear devices as far back as 1000 BC. The most probable uses were in clocks, temple devices and water-lifting equipment.

*Superscript numbers refer to items in the bibliography.

The earlier writings about gears did not write of gear devices as if they were new inventions; rather, the writings described gear devices with the implication that they were items of machinery or devices that were in common everyday use. It can thus be inferred that Greeks, Egyptians and Babylonians were using gear devices for many centuries prior to 300 BC. The discovery of the South Pointing Chariot proves that the Chinese had a knowledge and use of gearing going back as far as about 3000 BC.

After Aristotle, several ancient writers mentioned gears and left sketches (in some instances). Table 1 shows some of these.

Table 1 — **Early Gear Information**

Name	Approximate Date	Item
Aristotle	330 BC	Explains gear wheel drives in windlasses. Points out that the direction of rotation is reversed when one gear wheel drives another gear wheel.
Otesibius (Greek)	250 BC	Made water clocks and water organs using gears.
Philo of Byzantium	230 BC	Made rack and pinion device to raise water. Wrote of "elasticity" of metals. Tells how to test Spanish and Celtic swords.
Archimedes	220 BC	Made devices to multiply force or torque many times — studied spirals.

By 100 BC the gear art included both metal and wooden gears. Triangular teeth, buttressed teeth, and pin-teeth were all in use. Spur gears, racks and pinions and worm gears had all arrived on the scene. Right-angle pin-tooth drives were in use and perhaps the first primitive bevel gear.

Figure 4   South Pointing Chariot, circa 2600 BC. Courtesy of Smithsonian
             Institution, Washington, D.C.

8

Figure 5   Primitive gear types. Courtesy of L.O. Witzenburg, Cleveland Worm & Gear Division, Eaton Yale & Towne Inc., Cleveland, Ohio

Chapter 3

THE USE OF GEARING IN THE ROMAN EMPIRE
100 BC — 400 AD

As the Roman legions marched to conquer and develop the world's greatest empire, all the arts and crafts went through an extensive development. Gears were used for the first time to supply continuous power. Marcus Vitruvius, a colleague of Agrippa (writing about 16 BC), describes a flour mill driven by water power through right-angle gears (pin-gear type). See Fig. 6.

The Romans and Greeks made wide use of gearing in clocks and astronomical devices. Gears were also used to measure distance or speed. For instance, a small paddle wheel on the side of a ship was geared to a speed-indicating device. The ship was powered by oar or sail.

Hero of Alexandria wrote books describing the various hydraulic and mechanical devices used in the first* century AD. In his book, "Mechanics," he describes the five simple machines used to apply force to move a weight. These were the:

> wheel and axle
> lever
> pulley
> wedge
> screw

Hero wrote of gears but he apparently did not recognize them as a separate machine. For example, he shows a very practical arrangement of gear wheels for lifting a weight. Hero no doubt considered this as an advanced development of the wheel and axle machine.

A cyclometer device (hodometer) is shown by Hero. He says that the first wheel should be made of brass but neglects to specify material for the other parts of the gear train. This device (see Fig. 7) is believed to have been used as an attachment to a wagon wheel to measure a day's journey.

Hero worked to develop an advanced surveying instrument. Figure 8 shows his "dioptra."[2] Note the gear trains used for azimuth and elevation settings. Today's designers of radar pedestals should understand that they have a real "hero" as the pioneer of their art!

---

*The approximate date of his writings is established by an eclipse that was seen at 62 AD in Alexandria and noted by Hero.

Besides using gears to drive flour mills, the Romans (in Gaul) used gears to saw marble. Iron came into frequent use as a gear material. It is possible that the first case carburized gears were made by Romans.

An interesting device using a rack and a pinion is shown in Fig. 9. Hero describes this lamp and specifies that the rack should be made of *iron*.

One of the most interesting relics of this era is the "Antikythera" machine discovered by sponge divers off the Greek island of Antikythera. Recent studies by Derek Price, a British historian, reveal that this machine is an astronomical computer. The device was built about 82 BC (when Julius Caesar was a youth). The ship carrying it sank about 65 BC.

The Antikythera machine had many gear trains in it — some of which were planetary.[3] There was evidence of tooth breakage and repair of parts. Apparently the Romans had some gear troubles (just as we do today).

Figure 10 shows a schematic of the gear trains of the Antikythera machine as reconstructed by Rear Admiral Jean Theophanidis. Figure 11 shows some fragments of gearing of this machine as photographed by the National Museum, Athens. Note the triangular tooth shape. Some teeth are obviously worn or damaged. Others reveal the original tooth shape when new.

A very puzzling aspect of the Antikythera machine is that al-Birûna, an Iranian savant traveling in India wrote of a similar machine about 1000 years later. Did the technical know-how of this machine go from Rome to India and last for over a thousand years?

The Antikythera machine as well as the one in India had approximately 30-degree pressure angle teeth.

Figure 12 shows a segment of a Roman water clock gear. Note the interesting art work on the gear blank.

In the Roman era gears were first extensively used for power.* Hand cut gear teeth made in metal were frequently used. Pin wheel gears were still used extensively. A very wide variety of gear arrangements was used. Some of the gear arrangements invented in recent times were undoubtedly first used in Rome!

---

*There is evidence that the Chinese made some use of power gearing in the 4th century BC.

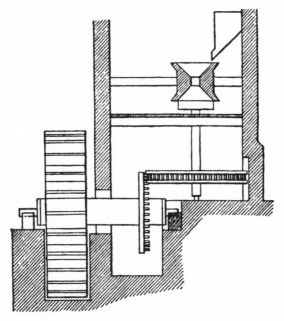

Figure 6   Schematic of Roman grist mill (as depicted by Marcus Vitruvius), circa 16 BC.

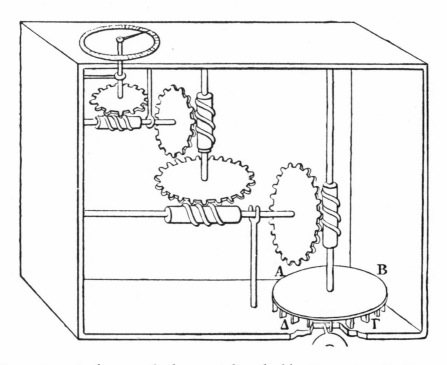

Figure 7   Cyclometer (hodometer) described by Hero, circa 62 AD.

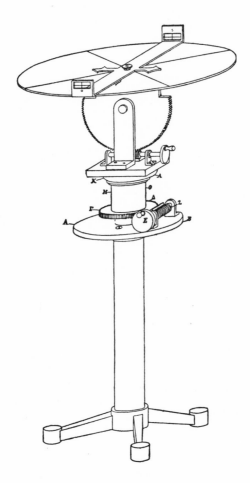

Figure 8   Hero's Dioptra, an early surveying instrument with azimuth and elevation gearing, circa 62 AD. (Reprinted by permission from "A History of Mechanical Inventions" by Abbott Payson Usher, Beacon Press, Beacon Hill, Boston, Massachusetts.)

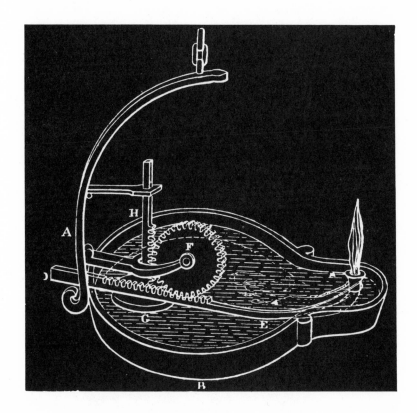

Figure 9   Ingenious Roman lamp with self adjusting wick; racks are iron.

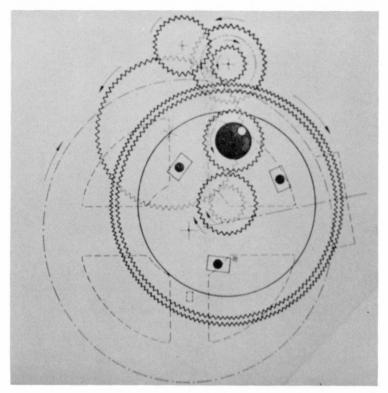

Figure 10   Schematic of Antikythera machine gearing by Theophanidis

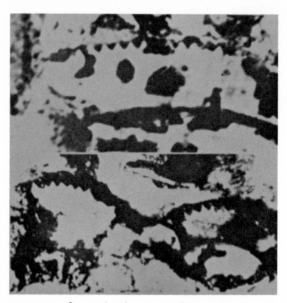

Figure 11   Fragments of Antikythera machine gears. Courtesy of National
Museum, Athens and Smithsonian Institution, Washington, D.C.

Figure 12　Segment of Roman water clock gear. Courtesy of Smithsonian Institution, Washington, D.C.

Chapter 4

GEAR USES AND DEVELOPMENTS THROUGH THE DARK AGES AND MEDIEVAL TIMES, 400 AD – 1600 AD

After the fall of Rome, there was a dark age in Western Europe. The center of learning moved to the Eastern Empire of Constantinople. (This empire lasted another thousand years!)

Not much is known about gearing in China but the gear art was apparently not lost there. Figure 13 shows a geared water clock of about 1090 AD. This complex clock measured time by the flow of water. Every 15 minutes the weight of water unlatched an "escape" wheel. This mechanism has been traced to 725 AD. The Chinese developed this device without any known contact with the Western world.

At the time of the Crusades, we find the Arabic world of Islam leading in mathematics and mechanical arts. Figure 14 shows a replica of a geared calendar assembly by Muhammed B. Abi Bakr of Isfahan, 1221-22 AD. The *original* gear assembly is in the Science Museum, London. This is believed to be the oldest workable set of gearing in existence. Furthermore, this drive is based on al-Birûna's design, circa 1000 AD. The al-Birûna design, as was noted earlier, undoubtedly goes back to the Antikythera machine of Roman times. Figure 15 shows the al-Birûna design.*

Most writers assume that the mechanical arts of Greece and Rome were lost to the world and then rediscovered. Several pieces of evidence indicate that they were never really lost. Many items of evidence, like the one above, indicate that technical knowledge was preserved in the Near East, India and Egypt and then reintroduced into Western Europe. The Moors, for instance, brought many technical ideas into Spain. Table 2 shows, in chronological order, the many developments in clock gearing, astronomical devices using gears and related gear devices.

Figure 16 shows an Islamic gear device used for pumping water. (The teeth shown look like they had better involute profiles than would normally be expected of a medieval Arab – probably the Smithsonian Institution redrew the old drawings with some improvements in details.)

*Figures 10, 11, 13, 15, 16, 17, 18 and Table 2, reproduced from the article "On The Origin Of Clockwork, Perpetual Motion Devices And The Compass" by Derek J. DeSolla Price in the United States National Museum Bulletin 218, *Contributions From The Museum of History and Technology,* published by the Smithsonian Institution, 1959. Figure 15 data came originally from E. Wiedemann's 1913 paper in *Der Islam,* 1913, Vol. 4, pg. 5.

18

Table 2 – CHRONOLOGICAL CHART

Classical Europe

3rd C., B.C. Archimedes planetarium
2nd C., B.C. Hipparchus Stereographic Projection
1st C., B.C., Vitruvius hodometer and water clocks
65, B.C. (ca.) Antikythera machine
1st C., A.D. Hero hodometer and water clocks
2nd C., A.D. Salzburg and Vosges anaphoric clocks

Islam

807 Harun-al-Rashid
850 (ca.) Earliest extamp astrolabes
1000 Geared astrolabe of al-Birūni
1025 Equatorium text
1150 Saladin clock
1200 (ca.) Ridwān water-clocks, perpetual motion and weight drive
1206 al-Jazari clocks, etc.
1221 Geared astrolabe
1232 Charlemagne clock
1243 al-Konpas (compass)
1272 Alfonsine corpus clock with mercury drum, equatoria

Europe

1000 Gerbert astronomical model
1187 Neckham on compass
1198 Jocelin on water clock
1245 Villard clocktower, "escapement," perpetual motion
1267 Villers Abbey clock
1269 Peregrinus, compass and perpetual motion
1271 Robertus Anglicus, animated models and "perpetual motion" clock
1285 Drover's water clock with wheel and weight drive
1300 (ca.) French geared astrolabe
1320 Richard of Wallingford astronomical clock and equatorium
1364 de Dondi's astronomical clock with mechanical escapement
later 14th C. Tradition of escapement clocks continues and degenerates into simple timekeepers

China

4th C., B.C. Power gearing
2nd C., A.D. Chang Hêng animated globe hodometer. Continuing tradition of animated astronomical models
725 Invention of Chinese escapement by I-Hsing and Liang Ling-tsan
1074 Shen Kua, clocks and magnetic compass
1080 Su Sung clock built
1101 Su Sung clock destroyed

India

1100 (ca.) Sūrya Siddhānta animated astronomical models and perpetual motion
1150 (ca.) Siddhānta Siromani animated models and perpetual motion

NOTE: This table is extracted from Reference 3 in the bibliography

Figures 17 and 18 show a French geared astrolabe and the details of the gear teeth. The tooth design is of a lower pressure angle (about 12°) and the teeth are slightly rounded (like an involute). This is a difference — and an improvement — over the straight sided, triangular teeth shown in Fig. 14. The teeth in clocks and watches, to this day, tend to have deep teeth with a low pressure angle. Clock gearing of this design is less apt to stick and bind due to tooth errors.

The French development of the astrolabe and English developments of the astrolabe and equatoria (Chaucer wrote a treatise on the astrolabe) can be traced to Arabic learning in the mechanical arts that flooded into Europe from about 1100 to 1300 AD.

The earliest mechanical clock for which the design has survived is the clock of Giovanni de Dondi of Padua, constructed 1348 to 1364. This imposing clock has been built again and put on display at the Smithsonian Institution in Washington, D.C., at their new Science and Technology building. Figure 19 shows the dial of Jupiter. The clock has four dials and an intricate gear and weight drive system. Figure 20 shows the weight and drive gearing for Dondi's clock.

Leonardo da Vinci, 1452-1519, designed all manner of things — including gear drives. This early-day genius designed battle cars, guns, cannons, a clockwork automobile and differential gears — among many other things. His notes have survived and provide an interesting insight into the mechanical knowledge and thinking of his day. Figure 21 shows a model of a da Vinci designed water pumping mill. Note pin-tooth gears.

One of the most notable developments of the early Middle Ages was the "lantern" pinion. This spur pinion had pins fixed at both ends. Thus it had much more load-carrying capacity. Figure 22* shows a drawing of a hand-driven grist mill using lantern pinions.

Figure 23 shows another example of a hand-driven grist mill. This example shows two sets of *speed reducing* gears and a set of *speed increasing* gears. In many cases, the ancient engineers made mistakes in their logic and designed things wrong. It is illogical to reduce speed and then increase speed in the same drive — unless one is just fascinated by gears!

Figure 24 shows some interesting gears including a worm gear drive and some sort of pounding machine to pulverize material. Obviously this machine wouldn't work. It is a *perpetual motion* machine. Water drives the big wheel but then is lifted by buckets to the upper trough so it can work again. Medieval engineers did not understand energy and friction loss

*Figures 22 through 27 were extracted from a book on machinery by George Andream Bocklern published in Nurnberg in 1661. An original copy of this book is preserved at the Smithsonian Institution.

principles. They kept designing many kinds of perpetual motion machines even though the machines would never work.

A practical machine is shown in Fig. 25. This machine uses water power to drive a boring tool. This was probably a wooden pipe making machine.

A grist mill driven by two persons walking in a large tread wheel is shown in Fig. 26. From medieval times down to the colonial days of the United States, tread mills were important power machines. People, horses, donkeys and goats were used in different kinds of tread mills. Troy, New York was prominent at one time in the manufacture of tread mills.

A grist mill driven by a medieval water turbine is shown in Fig. 27.

The first known gear cutting by machine was that developed by Juanelo Torriano (1501-1575) in constructing a great clockwork for Charles V of Spain. The device has about 1800 gear wheels. Torriano got up to a production rate of three wheels per day using a homemade, hand-powered gear-cutting machine. The cutter was in the form of a rotary file. Morales claims that Torriano's gear cutting device came into common use in Spain within 25 years' time. Morales'* account, translated by Woodbury, is very interesting.

"It took him as he told me, all of twenty years to conceive and work out the plan; and because of the great amount of energy and concentration in thinking about it, he got sick twice during that period and almost died. Then having spent so much time in conceiving it, it did not take him more than three and a half years to make it by hand. This was quite a feat because the whole clockwork (relox) had more than 1800 wheels not counting many other parts of iron and brass that are involved. So every day (not counting holidays), he had to make . . . more than three wheels that were different in size, number and shape of teeth, and in the way in which they are placed and engaged. But in spite of the fact that this speed is miraculous, even more astounding is a most ingenious lathe (torno) that he invented (and we see them today) to carve out with a file iron wheels (labrar ruedas de hierro con la lima) to the required dimensions and degree of uniformity of the teeth. And in spite of all this and knowing that he did it all by hand, it is not surprising that Januelo says, as he does, that no wheel was made twice because it always came out right the first time. And if all he said were not better in actual fact, it would be very surprising."

Gears in the medieval times were still rather crude. The learning of Rome slowly found its way into Western Europe. Crude mills were built. Clockwork made some notable progress. All in all, the medieval mechanic did not go much beyond the Roman of over 1000 years earlier. It is in the next interval that gearing began to develop rapidly.

*Reprinted from GEAR CUTTING by Robert S. Woodbury, pgs. 45-46 (see Ref. 4), by permission of the M.I.T. Press, Cambridge, Massachusetts.

Figure 13   A pictorial reconstruction of the astronomical clock-tower built by Su Sung and his collaborators at K'ai-fêng in Honan province, then the capital of the empire, in AD. 1090. The clockwork, driven by a water-wheel, and fully enclosed within the tower, rotated an armilliary sphere on the top platform and a celestial globe in the upper storey; puppet figures giving notice meanwhile of the passing hours and quarters by signals of sight and sound. (Original drawings by John Christiansen.) Courtesy of Smithsonian Institution, Washington, D.C.

Figure 14   Geared Astrolabe of 1221-22 AD by Muhammed B. Abi Bakr of Isfahan, from the Smithsonian, Washington, D.C.

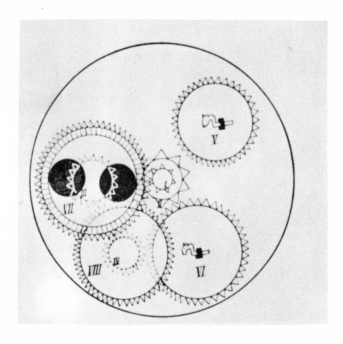

Figure 15   Calendrical gearing as designed by al-Birûna, circa 1000 AD.

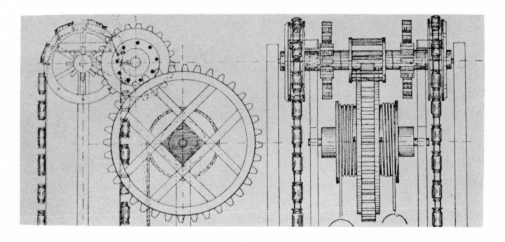

Figure 16   Islamic Water Pump driven by a weight drive, circa 1200 AD.

24

Figure 17   French Geared Astrolabe, circa 1300 AD.

Figure 18   Details of gear train in Fig. 17.

25

Figure 19   Dial of Jupiter, Dondi Clock from the Smithsonian Institution, Washington, D.C.

Figure 20   Weight and drive gears for Dondi Clock; note triangular teeth.
Courtesy of Smithsonian Institution, Washington, D.C.

Figure 21   Model of water pumping mill designed by Leonardo da Vinci. Courtesy of Museum of Science, Boston, Massachusetts.

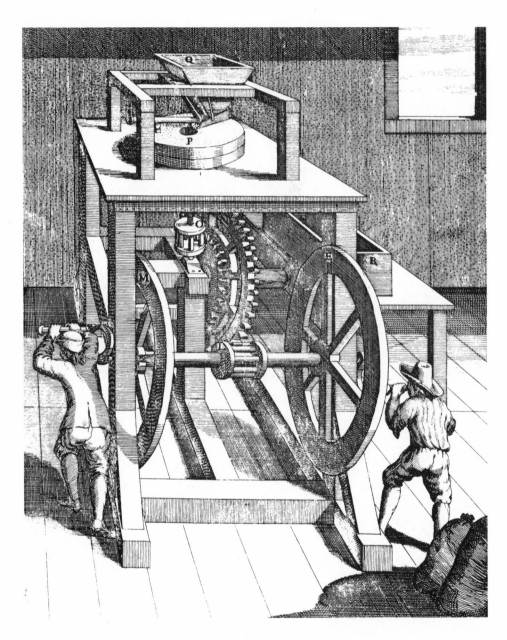

Figure 22   Lantern pinion used in grist mill drive, circa 1500 AD. Courtesy of Smithsonian Institution, Washington, D.C.

Figure 23   Small grist mill drive, circa 1500 AD. Courtesy of Smithsonian
Institution, Washington, D.C.

30

Figure 24   Medieval perpetual motion machine — not practical! Courtesy
of Smithsonian Institution, Washington, D.C.

Figure 25   Medieval machine to bore wooden pipe. Courtesy of Smithsonian Institution, Washington, D.C.

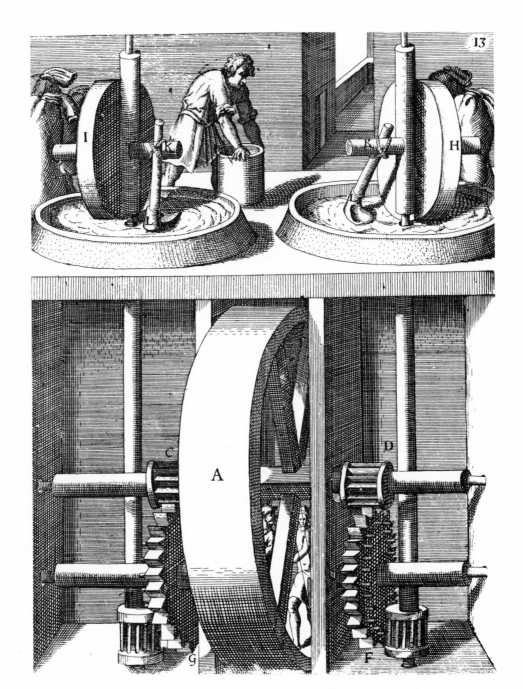

Figure 26   Tread wheel used to drive a grist mill. Courtesy of Smithsonian
Institution, Washington, D.C.

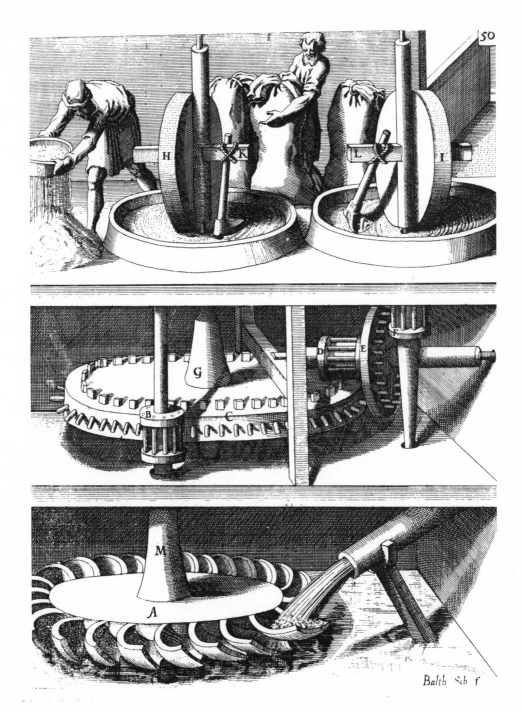

Figure 27   Water turbine used to drive a grist mill. Courtesy of Smithsonian Institution, Washington, D.C.

Chapter 5

THE BEGINNINGS OF MODERN GEARING
1600 AD — 1800 AD

In this period the theory of gear tooth action was first worked out. Theorists claimed — even then — that the involute tooth form should be used. Table 3 shows in capsule form some of the early work done on gear theory.

Table 3 — Gear Theorists

Name	Approx. Date	Nationality	Contribution
Nicholas of Cusa	1451	French	Studied cycloidal curve.
Albert Dürer	1525	German	Discovered epicycloids.
Girolamo Cardano	1557	Swiss	First mathematics of gears in print.
Philip de la Hire	1694	French	Full mathematical analysis of epicycloids. Recommended involute curve for gearing. (Involute not used in practice until about 150 years later.)
Charles Camus	1733	French	Expanded on work of la Hire, developed theories of mechanisms, studied lantern pinion and gear, crown gears and beveled gears.
Leonard Euler	1754	Swiss	Euler worked out design principles, worked out rules for conjugate action. Some consider him "the father of involute gearing."
Abraham Kaestner	1781	German	Wrote up practical methods for computing tooth shapes of epicycloid and involute gear teeth. Considered $15°$ to be a minimum pressure angle.
Robert Willis	1832	English	Wrote and taught extensively in gear field. A pioneer in gear engineering.
Edward Sang	1852	Scotch	General theory of gear teeth. Provided theoretical basis on which all gear tooth generating machines are based.

Most of the gears made in this period did not benefit much from the theories that a few people were writing about. Gear making was certainly a craft and an art. The skilled craftsman could make gears that would fit and run smoothly without having even heard of an involute or a cycloid. I have personally examined worm gear drives with the *gear driving the worm*. The tooth action was amazingly good considering the fact that gear cutting machines and gear checking machines would not show up for another century or more! (It should be added, of course, that some mighty crude cogwheels were being made in this period, too.)

Figure 28 shows epicyclic gear tooth drives of the kind designed by Camus. Note that two pairs of teeth are in contact even with only 5 teeth on the pinion. This means a contact ratio greater than 1.0. With *involute* teeth it is not practical to get a contact ratio over 1.0 with a 5 tooth pinion.

Woodbury makes the statement that Willis used a gear addendum equal to 1.0 divided by the diametral pitch. This is still the "standard" of the gear trade right down to present times. The origin of 14½° pressure angle is explained by Woodbury as follows:

"Willis comes to advocate the involute form from a study of the path of the point of contact and of the smallest number of teeth possible for spur gears, both external and internal, and for racks. This led him to consider the ideal working depth and addendum, as well as the thickness of the tooth and the breadth of space. He also introduced the constant 14½° because it had a sine of very close to ¼. Later this value was retained because it also coincided closely with the pressure angle usual in epicycloidal teeth. It is also the angle used for worm threads, too, making the straight-sided rack of the involute system correspond in angle, as well as in other proportions, with the worm thread. All this work was based upon pure mechanism.

"The result is a clear indication of the complexity resulting from epicycloidal teeth, especially for the cast teeth common at that time — separate molds would be required for each gear if they were to fit each other. Willis recognizes the limitations of the epicycloid for an interchangeable system of gearing. The advantages of the involute form stand out in the greater strength of this form, especially as compared to the epicycloidal with radial flanks." See Fig. 29.

An 18th century style of clock movement is shown in Fig. 30. This movement was made for a belfry of the German Reformed Church of Frederick, Md. where it was used until 1931. Its maker, Frederick Heisely, apparently learned his trade from George Hoff, his father-in-law, a European trained clock maker. This particular clock had a 14-foot pendulum.

During this period water power came into general use to drive relatively heavy duty mills. Figure 31 shows an example of a paper mill of about 1750 driven by a water wheel. This mill was about 65 miles south of Paris in l'Anglée. Mills like this made France an early leader in the production of paper.

Another water driven mill is shown in Fig. 32. Note the heavy duty gear wheels. These were made by inserting wooden teeth in cast iron hubs. The wooden teeth were generally made of maple.

The art of making metal gears for power drives really got going in this period. (Previously metal gears had been used primarily in clocks, instruments and just plain gadgets.) Figure 33 shows Eli Whitney's feed gearing drive for a milling machine. Whitney is most remembered for his invention of the cotton gin. After some years in the south (1792-1798), Whitney began the manufacture of firearms near New Haven, Connecticut. Whitney is noted for promoting the concept of interchangeable parts. This skilled craftsman and inventor made many important contributions to the mechanical arts.

John Stevens developed a multitubular boiler and a high pressure steam engine. He was concerned about safe and speedy transportation across the Hudson River (Stevens owned a New York to New Jersey ferry). Stevens' concern for his inventions led him to petition Congress for patent protection. Congress responded and passed the 1790 Patent Law, which is the foundation of our present patent system.

Stevens built a steamboat in 1802 with a *twin screw* drive. Figure 34 shows the gearing for Stevens' boat. Note that both Stevens and Whitney were using iron gears with about 5° pressure angle. (The improved 14½° teeth of Willis had not yet come into general use.)

38

Figure 28   Examples of epicyclic gear drives using a 5-tooth pinion. Courtesy of M.I.T. Press.

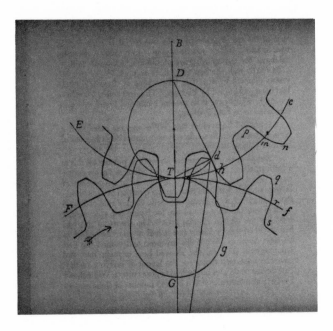

Figure 29   Old style involute teeth. Courtesy of M.I.T. Press.

Figure 30   An 18th century clock movement from Frederick, Md.
Courtesy of Smithsonian Institution, Washington, D.C.

40

Figure 31   French paper mill drive, circa 1750 AD.

41

Figure 32   Water driven mill, circa 1775 AD. Courtesy of Fortune Magazine.

42

Figure 33   Feed gearing in Eli Whitney's milling machine, circa 1800 AD. Courtesy of Smithsonian Institution, Washington, D.C.

43

Figure 34   Cast iron gears for twin screw drive in Stevens' steamboat, 1804 AD. Courtesy of Smithsonian Institution, Washington, D.C.

Chapter 6

THE MANY DEVELOPMENTS OF THE RECENT PAST
1800 AD – 1916 AD

Although gear cutting machines had gotten started in an earlier period, this period was the one in which most of the types which we know today got started. Table 4 shows in chronological form some of the more important machine developments.

Table 4 – **Some Early Landmarks in the Development of Machines to make Gear Teeth**

Kind of Machine	Name of Inventor or Developer	Approx. Date	Description
Gear Cutter	Juanelo Torriano	1540	Cut spur gears for a clock at a rate of three per day. Used rotary file instead of milling cutter. Hand powered.
Gear Cutter	Robert Hooke of England	1672	Cut spur gears with a formed wheel. Hand powered.
Gear Broaching Gear Cutting	Christopher Polhem of Sweden	1729	Machine to cut teeth with a reciprocating broach. Later developed machine to cut teeth with rotary cutters. Hand powered.
Gear Cutter	Henry Hindley of England	1741	Differential indexing. Rugged construction. Could cut pinions and racks. Hand powered.
Gear Cutter	Samuel Rehé	1783	Used true milling cutters rather than rotary file cutters. Cutters ground to approximate form for conjugate action. Hand powered.
Gear Cutter	J.G. Bodmer of Switzerland	1825	Made spur wheel cutting machines.

Table 4 — **Some Early Landmarks in the Development
of Machines to Make Gear Teeth (continued)**

Kind of Machine	Name of Inventor or Developer	Approx. Date	Description
Gear Cutter	Joseph Whitworth of England	1834	Involute cutters. Power driven by belt and pulley. Could cut spur and bevel gears.
Hobbing Machine	Joseph Whitworth of England	1835	Hobbed spiral gears. Whitworth took out first patents on the hob.
Gear Generator	Joseph Saxton of England	1842	Straight-sided milling cutter used to generate an involute tooth.
Gear Cutter	Joseph R. Brown of United States	1854	A "precision" machine for making index plates and master gears. Used "backed-off," form relieved cutter of modern type.
Bevel Gear Planing Machine	William Gleason of United States	1874	First practical bevel gear making machine built.
Bevel Gear Shaper	Hugo Bilgram of United States	1884	Used a generating type of process. Made bevel gears for bicycles.
Gear Cutter	H.E. Eberhardt (Gould & Eberhardt, USA)	1884	Patent on automatic indexing.
Hobbing Machine	Reinecker of Germany	1894	Heavy-duty machine.
Gear Shaper	E.R. Fellows (of Fellows Gear Shaper, USA)	1895	Gears cut by a "pinion" cutter with hardened and ground involute profile teeth.

Table 4 — **Some Early Landmarks in the Development of Machines to Make Gear Teeth (continued)**

Kind of Machine	Name of Inventor or Developer	Approx. Date	Description
Bevel Gear Generator	James E. Gleason (Gleason Works, USA)	1898	Rotary cutters used to generate bevel teeth. Automatic type of machine.
Hobbing Machine	Pfauter of Germany	1900	Hob axis could swivel. Differential gearing could be used.
Form Grinding	Ward and Taylor (Gear Grinding Machine Co., USA)	1908	Automatic, diamond point dressing of formed wheel. Spur gear making machine.

A gear cutting machine — believed to be Robert Hooke's — is shown in Fig. 35. The cutter, index mechanism and hand crank can all be seen. Note that even in this early machine, gears are used to make gears! Christopher Polhem's very nicely built machine for production gear cutting is shown in Fig. 36.

Figure 37 shows the oldest gear cutter that is still in existence. (Torriano's cutters are lost!) The French were very active in making horological machines (clocks) in the 18th century. Nicholas Bion (1652-1733) wrote of French gear cutting machines using formed rotary cutters.

The Brown & Sharpe Company of Providence, R.I., was an early pioneer in gear work in the United States. Figure 38 shows their first gear cutting machine. The well known Brown & Sharpe form cutter is shown in Fig. 39.

The great pioneer in the bevel gear field was William Gleason and the Gleason Works. Figure 40 shows the first bevel gear planer. The principle of the machine is depicted in Fig. 41.

Another bevel gear machine developer was Hugo Bilgram. His machine is shown in Fig. 42.

The bevel gear generator was developed by James E. Gleason, a son of William Gleason. The principle of his machine is shown in Fig. 43.

The gear cutting machines developed by Gould & Eberhardt achieved early fame. As early as 1889 these machines were being shipped all over the world. Figure 44* shows the spur gear cutting machine. By 1900 this type of machine had been developed to form cut helical gears. It also had (by then) an automatic return stroke. Eberhardt's pioneering work has had a lasting effect on the gear cutting industry that is still evident in many gear shops.

Although Table 4 does not show it, the first attempts had been made to generate grind gears with disk wheels and with threaded wheels. Woodbury states in the, "History of the Gear Cutting Machine," that by 1909 all the basic types of gear cutting machines had been built to use the grinding method.

In the period 1800-1916, the first elements of what we might call gear engineering or gear technology appeared. A little booklet written by Sereno Newton and published in 1832 by G.&C.&H. Carvill, New York City gives an interesting insight into the thinking of that period. The rule of Mr. James Carmichael is quoted for load carrying capacity:

"Rule. — Multiply the breadth of the teeth by the square of the thickness, and divide the product by the length; the quotient will be the proportionate strength in horses power, with a velocity of 2.27 feet per second."

The results of Mr. Carmichael's rule are shown in the following table in Sereno Newton's book.

Some very interesting — and very practical to this day — principles of gear design are given by Sereno Newton. The following is a good example:

"ON THE TEETH OF WHEELS"

"The proper method of forming the teeth of wheels so as to communicate equal motion, with as little friction as possible, is a matter of very great importance, and has given rise to much study among mechanics; the result of which shows that the faces of the teeth of wheels which are to act on one another, should be epicycloids. But as this is a curve not easily applied, parts of circles are frequently employed as a substitute. A straight line tending to the centre of the wheel appears to be the most advantageous form for the flank of the tooth, or that part which is within the pitch line as it causes least pressure on the axis. The proper form for the curved part of the tooth of a wheel or pinion to act on a rack is an involute of a circle, or, which

*Fig. 44 is from the April 1889 issue of Practical Mechanics, Worcester, Mass. Vol. II, No. 10.

Table 5

"PROPORTIONAL STRENGTH OF THE TEETH OF WHEELS, IN HORSES' POWER"

Calculated by Mr. Carmichael's Rule

Pitch in Inches	Thickness of Teeth in Inches	Breadth of Teeth in Inches	Length of Teeth in Inches	Horses' Power at 2.27 feet per Second	Horses' Power at 3 feet per Second	Horses' Power at 4 feet per Second	Horses' Power at 6 feet per Second	Horses' Power at 8 feet per Second	Horses' Power at 11 feet per Second
4.02	2.0	8.0	2.40	13.33	17.61	23.48	35.23	46.97	64.60
3.99	1.9	7.6	2.28	13.03	15.90	20.20	31.80	40.40	58.30
3.78	1.8	7.2	2.16	10.80	14.27	19.02	28.54	38.05	52.32
3.57	1.7	6.8	2.04	9.63	12.72	17.02	25.54	34.05	46.68
3.36	1.6	6.4	1.92	8.53	11.27	15.02	22.54	30.05	41.32
3.15	1.5	6.0	1.80	7.50	9.91	13.21	19.82	26.43	36.33
2.94	1.4	5.6	1.68	6.53	8.63	11.50	17.26	23.	31.64
2.73	1.3	5.2	1.56	5.63	7.44	9.92	14.88	19.84	27.28
2.52	1.2	4.8	1.44	4.80	6.34	8.45	12.68	16.91	23.24
2.31	1.1	4.4	1.32	4.03	5.32	7.09	10.64	14.19	19.54
2.10	1.0	4.0	1.20	3.33	4.40	5.87	8.81	11.75	16.15
1.89	.9	3.6	1.08	2.70	3.57	4.76	7.14	9.52	13.09
1.68	.8	3.2	.96	2.13	2.81	3.74	5.62	7.49	10.33
1.47	.7	2.8	.84	1.63	2.15	2.86	4.30	5.73	7.88
1.26	.6	2.4	.72	1.20	1.59	2.12	3.18	4.24	5.83
1.05	.5	2.0	.60	.83	1.10	1.46	2.20	2.93	4.03

NOTE: The strength being directly as the breadth, and the stress inversely as the velocity, it is easy to find the horses' power equal to any given breadth of these pitches; or the horses' power equal to any of these pitches and breadths, for any other velocity.

50

is the same, an epicycloid, whose generating circle is infinitely great; and the form of the teeth of a rack acting on a wheel or pinion is a cycloid. But as in the case of wheels acting on one another, parts of circles are generally used instead of these compound curves.

"A very common method of setting out the teeth of a wheel is to describe the teeth by a circular arc of which the radius is equal to the pitch added to half the thickness of the tooth, and of which the centre is the pitch line. Another method is to describe the teeth by an arc of which the radius is only equal to the pitch: but, in either case, the form of the teeth is better adapted to wheels that act as drivers, than to those that act as the driven, in consequence of the action of the teeth before they reach the line of centres.

"The friction of teeth approaching the line of centres is much greater than in receding* from it; and this is not the only disadvantage; for when a machine becomes worn it causes irregularity in its movements in consequence of the action in approaching the line of centres, tending to spread the axis of the wheels, while the action, in receding from that line, tends to draw these axis together, and consequently occasions more irregular action, friction, and wear, in the machine; therefore the teeth ought, if possible, never to begin to act before they arrive at the line of centres. But, in cases where the pinion is small, the action in approaching the line of centres cannot be altogether prevented. For it can be demonstrated that a pinion with less than ten teeth cannot be uniformly driven by a wheel of any number of teeth whatever, unless they act partly before they arrive at the line of centres: but a pinion of ten teeth may be moved uniformly by a wheel of 209 teeth; a pinion of eleven teeth, by a wheel having not less than 28 teeth; and a pinion of 12 teeth by a wheel having not less than 15 teeth; so that the whole of the action may be after the teeth arrive at the line of centres.

"When the pinion drives the wheel, the number of teeth on the pinion may be less, but it will not, in any case, be desirable to have less than 6 teeth on a pinion; and give the preference to 7 or 8, where it can be done with convenience.

"In all cases where it is admissible, the number of teeth in a wheel should be prime to the number of teeth in its pinion; that is, the number of teeth in the wheel should not be divisible by the number of teeth in the pinion. For example: Suppose there are 20 teeth in a pinion which is required to make about five revolutions to one of the wheel. If this were the exact ratio, there would be just 100 teeth in the wheel; and after each revolution of the wheel, the same teeth would be continually brought in contact. But, if the diameter of the wheel be made somewhat greater,—so as to admit of 101 teeth,—then after five revolutions of the pinion each tooth will come in contact with the one

*The advantages of "recess action" tooth design were appreciated even in 1832. There has been renewed interest in recess action gear designs in recent years.

on the wheel immediately before that on which it had worked at the commencement, and after five more revolutions will be engaged with the second tooth from those on which they acted in the first instance; therefore it is evident that the wheel must revolve 101 times, and the pinion 5 x 101 or 505 times before the same teeth will again come in contact. By this means the inequalities of wear, form, and material, will compensate each other."

One of the most noteworthy of the early pioneers of the gear industry was George B. Grant. This dynamic businessman founded no less than five gear companies in the United States. Three of these companies, Philadelphia Gear, Boston Gear Works and Grant Gear Works are still going strong today. George Grant was an inventor, a writer of gear books and an outstanding gear engineer. Grant is described[5] as having a flowing red beard and a commanding appearance somewhat like General U.S. Grant.

Some excerpts from Grant's book[6] called, "Gearing," give a good insight into the historical development of gears and gear engineering. The following is article 47 from the tenth edition of *Gearing* published by Grant Gear Works in 1907.

"THE MORTISE WHEEL"

"Another venerable relic of the last century is the "mortise" gear, having wooden teeth set in a cored rim, in which they are driven and keyed.

"Where a gear is subjected to sudden strains and great shocks, the mortise wheel is better, and works with less noise than a poor cast gear, and will carry as much as or more power at a high speed with a greater durability. But in no case is it equal of a properly cut gear, while its cost is about as great.

"In times where large gears could not be cut, and when the cast tooth was not even approximately of the proper shape, the mortise wheel had its place, but now that the large cut gear can be obtained the mortise gear should be dropped and forgotten."

Figures 31 and 32 show examples of mortise wheel gears. It is interesting to note that perhaps a hundred mills using mortise gears are still in operation in the United States right now in 1968.

The business of making replacement teeth for these mills is mostly handled by the Thompson Manufacturing Company of Lancaster, New Hampshire. In 1967, President Robert D. Hilliard showed the writer through the plant and explained that there was still a very active business in supplying maple gear teeth (literally tens of thousands per year) for use primarily in paper mills, roofing mills and grist mills for customers in nearly every state east of the Rocky Mountains. Many old mills are scattered throughout New England, upstate New York and Pennsylvania. Most of these mills are still using water power and are carrying on enterprises that go back over 100 years. The Thompson Manufacturing Company (incidentally) was established in 1858.

At the time of my visit several hundred finished maple gear teeth were in the shipping room ready for shipment and a whole stack of unfilled orders were in the plant.

In article 51 of his book, Grant gives an interesting story about how to figure horse-power for cast gears.

"HORSE-POWER OF CAST GEARS"

"The horse-power of a gear is the amount of power it may be depended upon to carry in continual service.

"It is very well settled that continual strains and impact will change the nature of the metal, rendering it more brittle, so that a tooth that is perfectly reliable when new may be worthless when it has seen some years of service. This cause of deterioration is particularly potent in the case of rough cast teeth, for they can only approximate to the true shape required to transmit a uniform speed, and the continual impact from shocks and rapid variations in the power carried must and does destroy the strength of the metal.

"There are about as many rules for computing the power of a gear as there are manufacturers of gears, each foundryman having a rule, the only good one, which he has found in some book, and with which he will figure the power down to so many horses and hundredths of a horse as confidently as he will count the teeth or weigh the casting.

"Even among the standard writers on engineering subjects, the agreement is no better, as shown by Cooper's collection of twenty-four rules from many different writers, applied to the single case of a five-foot gear. See the "Journal of the Franklin Institute" for July, 1879. For the single case over twenty different results were obtained, ranging from forty-six to three hundred horse-power, and proving conclusively that the exact object sought is not to be obtained by calculations.

"This variety is very convenient, for it is always possible to fit a desired power to a given gear, and if a badly designed gear should break, it is a simple matter to find a rule to prove that it was just right, and must have met with some accident.

"Although no rule can be called reliable, the one that appears to be the best is that given by Box, in his Treatise on Mill Gearing. Box's rule, which is based on many actual cases, and which gives among the lowest, and therefore the safest results, is by the formula:

$$\text{Horse-power of a cast gear} = \frac{12\,c^2\,f\sqrt{d\,n}}{1{,}000}$$

in which c is the circular pitch, f is the face, d is the diameter, all in inches, and n is the number of revolutions per minute.

"Example: A gear of two feet diameter, four inches face, two inches pitch, running at one hundred revolutions per minute, will transmit

$$\frac{12 \times 2 \times 2 \times 4 \times \sqrt{24 \times 100}}{1{,}000} = 9.4 \text{ h.p.}$$

"For bevel gears, take the diameter and pitch at the middle of the face.

"It is perfectly allowable, although it is not good practice, to depend upon the gear for from three to six times the calculated power, if it is new, well made, and runs without being subjected to sudden shocks and variations of load.

"The influence of impact and continued service will be appreciated when it is considered that the gear in the example, which will carry 9.4 horse-power, will carry seventy horse-power if impact is ignored, and the ultimate strength of the metal is the only dependence.

"A mortise gear, with wooden cogs, will carry as much as, or more than a rough cast-iron gear will carry, although its strength is much inferior. The elasticity of the wood allows it to spring and stand a shock that would break a more brittle tooth of much greater strength. And, for the same reason, a gear will last longer in a yielding wooden frame than it will in a rigid iron frame."

In the example shown, the 24″ gear running at 100 RPM with 4″ face width and a 2″ circular pitch would have had a unit *load* index of 194 psi at the 9.4 HP allowed. AGMA 225.01 shows 5000 psi as design limit for s_{at} for low grade cast iron. For a slow speed cast tooth of this size a stress limit of 5000 psi would make the allowable unit load come out to be about 400 for $14\frac{1}{2}°$ pressure angle teeth of the old style. This shows that Grant was advocating design loads that would look reasonable by modern methods.

The data of 1832 given by Sereno Newton calculates to have an allowable unit load for cast iron of 300 and an allowable unit load for wood of 75. These values are not too different than those used by Grant almost 100 years later. The big difference to be noted was that Grant was worried about the effects of impact and the fatigue (and wear) due to long time operation. Grant's recommended formula has the effect (due to the square root sign) of *severly derating* the higher speed gears.

The period 1800-1916 showed a great expansion in the use of gears. Gears were used for the first time in ship propulsion, bicycles, textile mills, machine tools, automobiles, and even in the early airplane. Older uses in guns, clocks, process machinery, etc. were greatly expanded.

The gears cut in the early part of the nineteenth century showed a marked improvement in both design and craftsmanship. Figure 45 shows the gear drives used to turn the 10-foot lens at the historic Navesink Light on the New Jersey coast. With 9,000,000 candle power, Navesink (erected in 1828) was the most powerful lighthouse in the United States in its day. Note the rather good looking spur and bevel gears — made before modern gear cutting machines were invented! Note also that *lantern* pinions were still used.

54

Figure 35   Robert Hooke's wheel cutting engine, circa 1672 AD. Courtesy of the Science Museum, London

Figure 36   Christopher Polhem's machine to cut clock work gears, circa 1729 AD. Courtesy of Smithsonian Institution, Washington, D.C.

56

Figure 37   The "oldest" gear cutter. Courtesy of Brown & Sharpe.

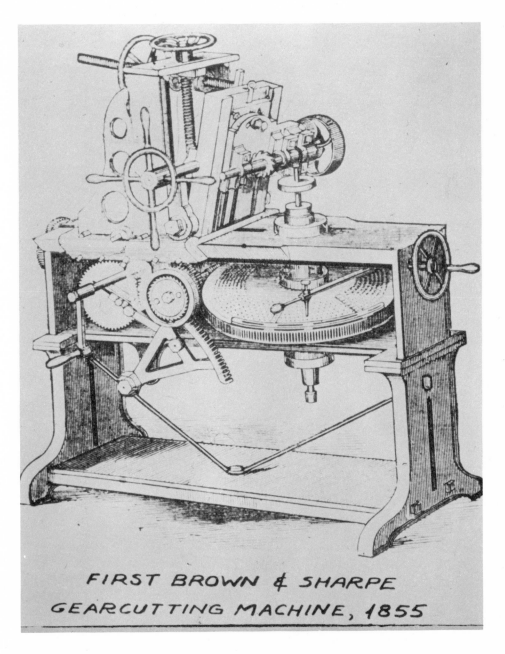

Figure 38   First Brown & Sharpe gear cutting machine, 1855 AD.

Figure 39   Brown & Sharpe form relieved gear cutter.

59

Figure 40   Gleason bevel gear planing machine. Courtesy of the Gleason Works, Rochester, New York.

60

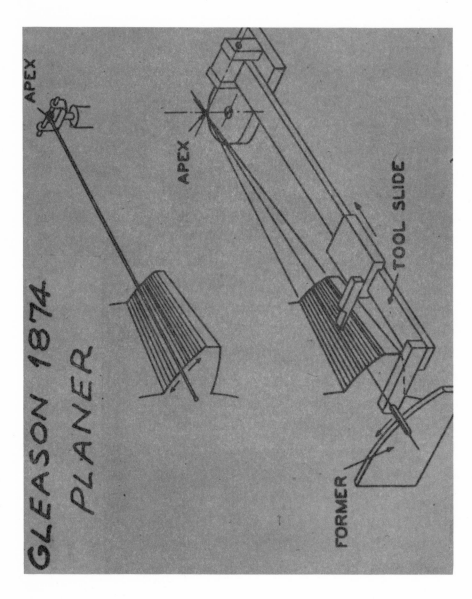

Figure 41   Principle of Gleason bevel gear planing machine. Courtesy of the Gleason Works, Rochester, New York.

61

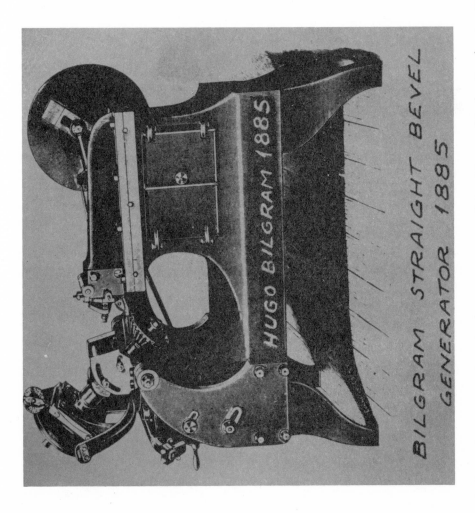

Figure 42   Bilgram gear generator, 1885 AD. Courtesy of the Gleason Works, Rochester, New York.

62

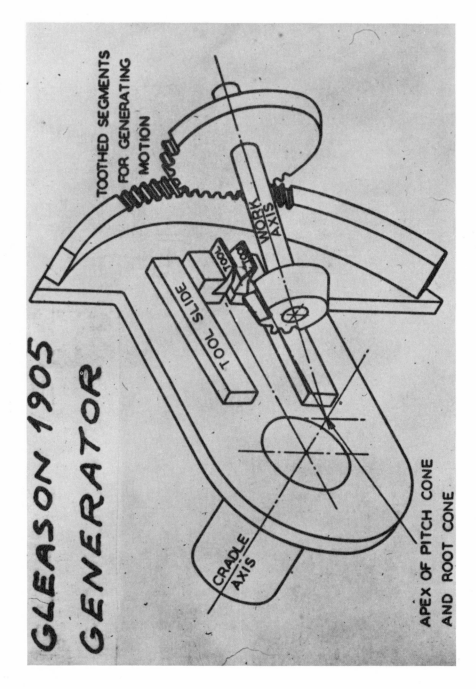

Figure 43   Gleason bevel gear generator. Courtesy of the Gleason Works, Rochester, New York.

EBERHARDT'S FULL AUTOMATIC GEAR CUTTER.

Figure 44   Eberhardt's automatic gear cutting machine, circa 1889 AD.

Figure 45   Gear drives used at Navesink Lighthouse, circa 1828. Courtesy
of Museum of Science, Boston, Massachusetts.

Chapter 7

THE GREAT UPSURGE OF THE GEAR ART IN THE
HALF CENTURY OF AGMA, 1916 AD – 1968 AD

So much progress has occurred in the gear art in the last fifty years that it is difficult to describe it in a few words.

The first models of most of the machine tools used in the gear trade had appeared by 1916. The 1915 model, though, compared with the 1968 model is like comparing a 1915 Model T Ford with the Oldsmobile Toronado of today!

New additions to the family of gear machine tools in the last fifty years include gear shaving machines, *Shear-speed machines, gear honing machines, bevel gear grinding machines, worm thread grinders, helical gear grinders and machines to broach splines or gears.

Besides the vast improvements made in the machine tools, to make gear teeth, a whole family of machine tools has appeared to measure gear teeth. These include involute checkers, lead checkers, composite error checkers and spacing checkers. Very recently the Fellows Gear Shaper Company and Hofler (of Germany) have each made breakthroughs on machines to rapidly measure index error (accumulated tooth spacing).

The man running a modern gear shop will often comment rather ruefully that it costs as much to tool up and measure gears as it does to make them in the first place!

Both gear making and gear checking have become highly automated. In the large production plants for automotive gearing, it can be said truthfully that the gear is made, measured and then accepted or rejected *untouched by human hands*.

Although basic involute theory for parallel axis gears was worked out long ago, much work remained to be done to settle the mathematics of *any tooth shape* meshing *on any skew, right-angle* or *nonintersecting axis*. The difficult mathematics of gears and gear cutting for *any tooth form* on *any axis* has been almost completely solved. Some of the better known contributors to this work of modern gear theory are Ernest Wildhaber, Earle Buckingham, H.E. Merritt (England), Allen Candee, Werner Vogel, Hillel Poritsky, G. Niemann (Germany), Darle Dudley, Oliver Saari, Charles B. King and Meriwether Baxter.

*Trademark of Michigan Tool Company (Division of Ex-Cell-O Corp.), Detroit, Michigan

66

Seventy-five years ago the load rating of gears was handled by very simple rules. That great pioneer in American gear work, George Grant, had tried to make a little order of chaos and had set down rules for wooden gear teeth, cast iron teeth and steel teeth. Wilfred Lewis presented a technique which is still the basis of most gear strength calculations. (This was about 1900 AD.)

The early builders of power gears were concerned with the fact that errors in gear teeth produced dynamic loads and made a fast running gear unable to carry as much torque as a slow running gear. The historical turning point in gear engineering relative to dynamic load came in 1931 when a research committee of the American Society of Mechanical Engineers—under the chairmanship of Earle Buckingham—published the results of an extensive gear test program. The results of this work gave test data on dynamic load and led to the establishment of formulas to calculate dynamic loads. These methods have been widely published* and used.

In recent years investigators have made much more sophisticated dynamic load tests. The fear of dynamic loads has led gear designers and gear manufacturers to become greatly concerned about gear accuracy. It soon became clear to the whole gear trade that gears had to be made to great precision if they were to run fast and last a long time. In modern turbine drives the first reduction generally has a pitch line speed of more than 10,000 feet per minute. Typical gears in a 5-year period will run for as much as 10 billion contact cycles without serious wear! The old cast iron gears of a hundred years earlier often had trouble running a year at 500 feet per minute.

Modern research and development testing plus a large amount of field experience has led to a whole stable of sophisticated rating formulas[9] for spur, helical, bevel and worm gears. Gears are rated for strength, surface durability — and if necessary — given a thermal rating and a scoring rating. Some of the better known men in gear rating work of the last fifty years are Aubrey Ross, Walter Schmitter, John Almen, Earle Buckingham, Darle Dudley, Edward Wellauer, G. Niemann, John Seabrook, Bruce Kelley, Martin Hartman, H. E. Merritt, Eugene Shipley, Paul Gustafson, S. L. Crawshaw and Wells Coleman.

The dramatic progress in gear load carrying capacity can be seen if we look at the Table 6 list of *unit load*** values. (The unit load index of tooth

*See Item 8 in the bibliography for dynamic load calculation methods.

$$**\text{Unit load} = \frac{\text{tan driving force} \times \text{diam. pitch}}{\text{face width} \times \text{cosine of helix angle}} = \frac{W_t \times P_d}{F \times \text{Cos } \psi}, \text{ psi}$$

strength is the only criterion of rating that goes back to 1800. Other index criteria such as *K-Factor, scoring factor,* etc. were not used until the early 1900's.)

If we compare a good wood tooth of 1800 with a good rocket gear tooth of 1968, there is a gain in ability to carry tooth loads of about 400 to 1! Even in ferrous metal the gain from cast teeth of 1800 to steel rocket gear teeth of 1968 is a good 100 to 1!

The gains in tooth load carrying capacity have resulted from improvements in gear metallurgy[9,10] and lubricants as much as from design improvements and accuracy improvements. Highly alloyed steels and cast irons came into wide use about 1920. Nitriding and improved case hardening developed rapidly from about 1930 onwards. Induction hardening of gear teeth came into use about 1950. Vacuum melt steels of unusual purity came into general use about 1960.

Table 6 — Comparison of Typical Maximum Unit Load Values Used in Design

Approx. Date	Kind of Application	Approximate Unit Load in p.s.i.	Material
1832	water-powered mill	75	hard wood
	water-powered mill	300	cast iron, as cast
1900	steam engine	1100	cast iron, cut teeth
1968	electric motor	5000	high strength cast iron, precision machined
	steam turbine	6000	steel gears, precision machined
	steam turbine	9000	hardened steel gears, precision machined
	aircraft gas turbines	15,000	case hardened and precision ground
	rocket engine	30,000	case hardened, super quality steel, ground to extreme accuracy

"Extreme pressure" lubricants for hypoid (and other gears) were first used around 1930. Several very sophisticated oil additives came into use in the 1955-1960 period. Synthetic lubricants for hot running gas turbine engines and gears have developed rapidly since 1950. A wide array of special lubricants permit gears to operate under load, temperature and speed conditions that would have otherwise been impossible.

During the 1916-1966 period, the 20° pressure angle involute teeth with extra depth to provide a full-fillet, root radius became the general standard of the gear industry. For extra heavy load carrying capacity, 25° pressure angle teeth became popular. Tooth designers frequently made the pinion *long addendum* and the gear *short addendum* to improve load carrying capacity. Figure 46 shows a modern design with very high load carrying capacity.

The old 14½° involute remained in use but was not the most popular design. Epicyclic teeth passed out of use except for a few special cases.

Some new tooth forms and arrangements have appeared in the last fifty years. These include the Formate R[1] gear tooth, the Wildhaber-Novikov tooth form, and Spiroid R[2] kinds of gears, the Harmonic Drive R[3] and Cone-Drive R[4] gears. The hypoid gear was known before 1916 but it took machine tool developments and automotive needs of the 1920-1930 era to push it into high production. Ernest Wilhaber and the Gleason Works did the pioneering in gear machinery development and gear geometry to make the modern hypoid gear practical.

The newcomers just mentioned are either already important in the gear market place, or they have a potential which makes them important to consider. It seems probable that there will be even more tooth forms and tooth kinds to consider in the near future.

The work of AGMA has led to standards, information sheets, and technical investigations covering the whole gamut of gear technology. (See Page 89.) This work has become the unquestioned authority for responsible design and application of gearing in the United States. Outside the United States, AGMA work is studied (and often followed) by those concerned with the design and application of gearing. No other country has come even close to the work done by AGMA in the United States in advancing and codifying gear technology.

[1] Formate is a trademark of the Gleason Works, Rochester, New York

[2] Spiroid is a trademark of the Illinois Tool Works Inc., Chicago, Illinois

[3] Harmonic Drive is a trademark of the United Shoe Machinery Co., Beverly, Mass.

[4] Cone-Drive is a trademark of the Michigan Tool Company, Detroit, Michigan

Figure 46   Involute teeth of modern design.

Chapter 8

THE PIONEERING OF TODAY PORTENDS
THE TRENDS OF TOMORROW

In laboratories and shops all over the United States (and the world) new things are being tried or built for the first time. This is true for the field of gearing just as it is true in so many other fields. Out of this pioneering work will come the new things of tomorrow.

In many areas, significant new developments are taking place that will be very important in the future. These are:

giant gears
huge gear teeth
ultra-tiny gear teeth
hard gears in very large sizes
gears to run at high load without oil
noiseless gears (almost noiseless)
gears to run at 1000 °F
gears to run in nonlubricating fluids
new tooth forms beyond involute, cycloid, Wildhaber-Novikov
new knowledge of stress pattern in odd-shaped gear teeth
new knowledge of scoring phenomena
gears and splines formed by rolling
toothed gears formed by high energy forging
electron beam welding of *finished* parts of a gear assembly
statistical reliability data as a full-fledged tool of gear design

A large gear used to be one almost 200 inches in diameter (16.7 feet). Now some gears are being made in the giant range of 70 to 100 feet in diameter. Since no machine tools are this large, the gear wheels are being made in sectors and assembled into wheels. Earle Gear, Philadelphia Gear, Brad Foote, Sewall Gear (and possibly others) have been active in this field. The colossal 500-foot gear is probably just around the corner! Figure 47 shows a pinion and a segment of a gear having over 100 foot pitch diameter. Figure 48 shows a large radio telescope. Note the giant segment gear used for elevation drive. A segment of a radar gear for a deep space probe unit is shown in Fig. 49.

It is still very difficult to cut a gear tooth coarser than 3/4 pitch. Lufkin Foundry and Machine Company have recently made some very well-formed gear teeth twice this big at 3/8 pitch. See Fig. 50.

The finest pitch used to be around 128 pitch. Gears are now being made in the 200 to 400 pitch range. Fellows Gear Shaper is one of the pioneers in this field. In contrast to the giant gears and gear teeth just mentioned, note the very tiny gears in Figs. 51 and 52.

Most companies still consider a gear around 30-inch diameter as the upper limit for case carburizing without too much distortion. A few have handled 50-inch gears via case carburizing. Recently, Brad Foote successfully carburized a 72-inch gear. See Fig. 53 for a 54-inch carburized gear.

Large, wide face helical pinions are perhaps the most difficult parts to harden without excessive distortion. Unusual skill and very special heat treat facilities have been developed by Tool Steel Gear and Pinion in making extra heavy duty gearing for steel mills. Figure 54 shows a pair of pinions that were carburized and hardened with a case depth of over .150″. These pinions — for a steel mill pinion stand — are so accurate after hardening that satisfactory contact can be obtained over a tooth height of about 2 inches and a face width of over 5 feet without grinding. The ability to make hard gears this large without significant distortion is a remarkable new development in the gear trade.

Gears in large sizes are being nitrided successfully. One Swiss company claims to be making good 100-inch gears by nitriding. In the United States 60 inches is still about the limit for nitriding facilities.

Spline forming and worm thread forming by rolling have become well established production processes. Gear teeth are harder to make because of the deeper tooth depth but gear tooth rolling is beginning to become a new production process. Figures 55 and 56 show the start and near finish of a gear rolling operation.

High energy forging can make hot steel flow into a die almost like molten metal. Very powerful new forging machines will now form gear teeth and other parts with an accuracy and complexity that was only previously possible in precision die forgings of nonferrous metals (zinc, for instance). The forged gear can use very high strength steel and make a part that is as good or better than a high strength machined part.

Figure 57 shows an example of a gear with teeth finish forged. The spacing and lead accuracy are around AGMA quality level 8. With further development, it is probable that many small gears can be finish forged to as high as AGMA quality level 10. (Incidentally, forged gears have to have the "flash" trimmed off the ends of the teeth and the bores or journals finish ground.)

For very high accuracy gears of the future, the *high energy* forging of gear teeth could readily be teamed up with a finishing operation only of shaving or grinding to get accuracy in the AGMA quality level 12 to 14.

The pioneering work of Dynamic Forge Corporation has shown that high energy forging can be used to advantage in several ways in the gear trade. For instance, a complex jet engine gear can be forged to shape in one blow. (See Fig. 58.) A minimum amount of premium steel is used and an unusually good structure is obtained.

Figure 59 shows how a blank shape, complicated to machine, can be readily produced by forging. At present the internal teeth and splines are cut. With more development of the process and die, it will soon become possible to make complex parts, teeth and all, by this remarkable new process.

Gears (of any size) are being induction hardened a tooth at a time. Philadelphia Gear and National Automatic Tool are both very active in this field. See Figs. 60 and 61.

Military people need capability to run their helicopters (or other equipment) for a few hours after they have been shot up. They want to get home! Advanced work on how to run gearing at high load without oil is being done at Mechanical Technology Inc. in Latham, New York, Bell Helicopter, Ft. Worth, Texas and by the Vertol Division of the Boeing Company in Morton, Pennsylvania. Peculiar steel compositions and special tooth surface treatments make it possible to run at high load without oil.

In many situations, powerful gears do everything that is desired of them but they make enough noise to impair human hearing. Pioneering work in noise reduction is being done by General Electric, De Laval, Mechanical Technology and others. The gear of the future must be a gentleman who speaks with a soft voice. It is becoming uncouth to aggravate people and impair their hearing with noisy, ill-mannered gears!

We can look to a steady advancement in all the areas of gear development mentioned above (plus many other areas). The next fifty years will certainly turn out to be even more surprising than the last fifty.

Those of us in the gear field can be most proud that our product has been around for about five thousand years and is *here to stay*. We have one of the finest trade associations in the world, "AGMA." Gear manufacturers and gear engineers under AGMA leadership will continue to match progress in other fields with outstanding progress in the very important field of gearing.

74

Figure 47 Segment of an internal gear of slightly over 100 feet pitch diameter. Pinion is 24 teeth, 1-½ pitch, 10" face width and 20° pressure angle. Courtesy of Sewall Gear Manufacturing Company, St. Paul, Minnesota.

Figure 48   Radio telescope. Note very large gear segment. Courtesy of Sewall Gear Manufacturing Company and Blaw-Knox Company.

76

Figure 49   Checking a segment of an 80 foot gear for a deep space radar unit. Courtesy of Philadelphia Gear Corporation, King of Prussia, Pennsylvania.

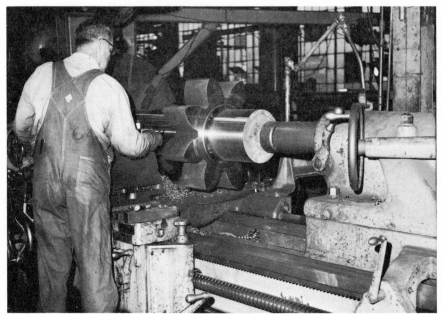

Figure 50   Finishing an 8-tooth pinion, 3/8 pitch, 21.333" pitch diameter, 6" face width. This pinion was made by torch cutting and is used to drive a giant rack on an offshore drilling platform. Courtesy of Lufkin Foundry & Machine Co., Lufkin, Texas.

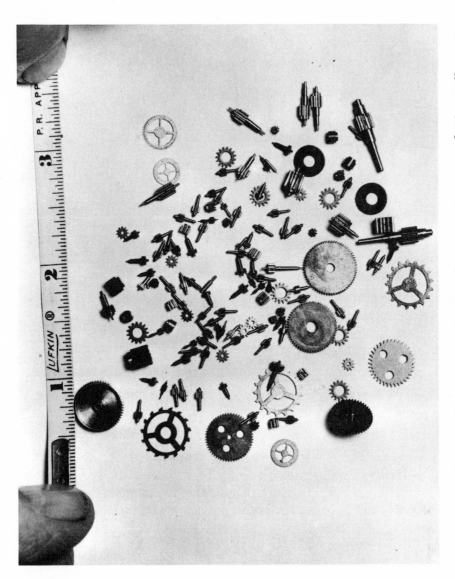

Figure 51 An assortment of very fine pitch pinions and gears. Courtesy of The Fellows Gear Shaper Co., Springfield, Vermont.

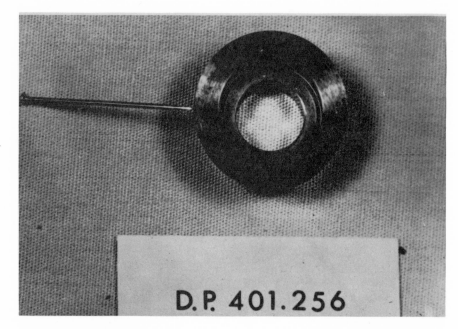

D. P. 401.256

Figure 52   A gear with teeth so tiny that they cannot be seen without a
magnifying glass. Note weave of cloth and tiny brad for
comparison — 401.256 pitch. Courtesy of The Fellows Gear
Shaper Company, Springfield, Vermont.

Figure 53   A 54″ gear carburized and finished without grinding passes contact test with its pinion. Courtesy of Brad Foote Gear Works, Inc., Chicago, Illinois.

80

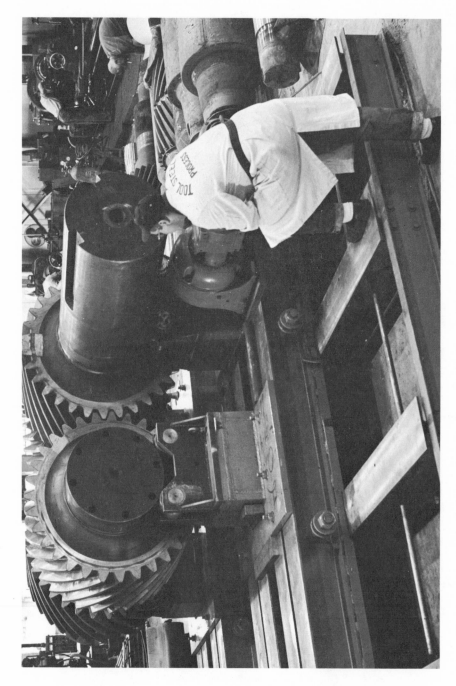

Figure 54 Giant carburized pinions, ¾″ pitch — 68″ face width pass contact test without grinding. Courtesy of Tool Steel Gear and Pinion Company, Cincinnati, Ohio.

Figure 55   Start of a rolled gear. Courtesy of Michigan Tool Company, Detroit, Michigan.

Figure 56   Gear in Fig. 55 almost finish rolled.

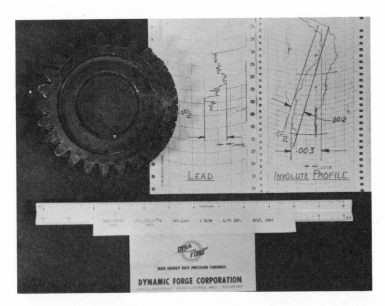

Figure 57   Experimental helicopter gear finish forged in one blow. Weight
is 4.75 lbs. Courtesy of Dynamic Forge Corporation, Royal
Oak, Michigan.

Figure 58   Blank for jet engine gear made in one blow. Bar of stock is
shown at left and cross section of this very intricate gear is
shown at right. Courtesy of Dynamic Forge Corporation, Royal
Oak, Michigan.

84

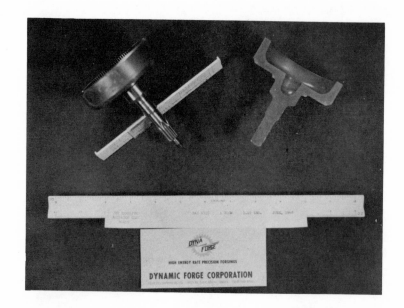

Figure 59   Actuator gear blank for jet transport is made in one blow. Part weighs 1.49 lbs. Forged blank is shown on the right — finish gear is shown on left. Courtesy of Dynamic Forge Corporation, Royal Oak, Michigan.

85

Figure 60   Large gear teeth induction hardened by scanning a tooth at a time with a moving induction coil. Courtesy of Philadelphia Gear Corporation, King of Prussia, Pennsylvania.

Figure 61   Induction hardening a large pinion. Courtesy of Philadelphia
Gear Corporation, King of Prussia, Pennsylvania

BIBLIOGRAPHY

1. De Camp, L. Sprague, "The Ancient Engineers," Doubleday & Co., Garden City, New York, 1963

2. Usher, Abbott Payson, "A History of Mechanical Inventions," Beacon Press, Boston, Massachusetts, 1929

3. Smithsonian Institution, "Contributions from the Museum of History and Technology," Bulletin 218, 1959

4. Woodbury, Robert S., "History of the Gear Cutting Machine," M.I.T. Press, Massachusetts Institute of Technology, Cambridge, Massachusetts, 1959

5. Ball, Russell C., Jr., Newcomen Society Speech, January 1963

6. Grant, George B., "Gear Wheels," Grant Gear Works, Boston, Massachusetts

7. Buckingham, Earle, "Dynamic Loads on Gear Teeth" (Report of the ASME Special Research Committee on the Strength of Gear Teeth), American Society of Mechanical Engineers, New York, 1931

8. Buckingham, Earle, "Analytical Mechanics of Gears," Dover Publications, Inc., New York, 1963

9. Dudley, Darle W., "Gear Handbook," McGraw-Hill Book Company, New York, 1962

10. Dudley, Darle W., "Size of Gear Sets," *Product Engineering,* Vol. 35, No. 23, pp. 92-102, November, 1964

11. Buckingham, Earle, "Involute Spur Gears," Niles-Bement Pond Company, New York, 1922

12. Williams, H. A., "History of Power Transmission" AGMA Paper 029.02, June 1950

13. Flanders, Ralph E., "Gear-Cutting Machinery," John Wiley & Sons, New York, 1909

14. Manchester, H. H., "Early Traces of the Toothed Wheel," *American Machinist,* December 16, 1920 (Vol. 53, No. 25) and December 23, 1920

15. Seabrook, John B., and Dudley, Darle W., "Results of a Fifteen-Year Program of Flexural Fatigue Testing of Gear Teeth," *Journal of Engineering for Industry,* pp. 221-237, August, 1964

16. Dudley, Darle W., "The Phenomenal Growth of Aerospace Gear Art," *Power Transmission Design,* February, 1966

17. Dudley, Darle W., "The Evolution of the Gear Art, circa 1966," AGMA Paper 990. 14, June, 1966

AGMA Standards and Technical Publications

NOMENCLATURE

Gear-Tooth Wear and Failure (USAS B6.12-1964)
Terms, Definitions, Symbols, and Abbreviations
Reference Information — Gear-Specification Drawings
Information Sheet — Formats for Fine-Pitch Gear Specification Data
Reference Information — Basic Gear Geometry

TOOLS, CUTTERS AND HOBS

Single-Thread Coarse-Pitch Hobs
Single-Thread Fine-Pitch Hobs
Multiple-Thread Coarse-Pitch Hobs
Wormgear Hobs

APPLICATION

Application Classification for Spur, Helical, Herringbone and Bevel Gear Gearmotors
Application Classification for Helical, Herringbone and Spiral Bevel Gear Speed Reducers
Application Classification for Spur, Helical, and Herringbone Gear Shaft Mounted Speed Reducers

GEAR SYSTEMS

Tooth Proportions for Coarse-Pitch Involute Spur Gears (USAS B6.1-1968)
System for Zerol Bevel Gears
Fine-Pitch On-Center Face Gears for 20-Degree Involute Spur Pinions
Tooth Proportions for Fine-Pitch Involute Spur and Helical Gears (USAS B6.7-1967)
System for Straight Bevel Gears (USAS B6.13-1965)
System for Spiral Bevel Gears

DURABILITY

Surface Durability (Pitting) of Spur Gear Teeth
Surface Durability (Pitting) of Helical and Herringbone Gear Teeth
Rating for the Durability of Helical and Herringbone Gears for Enclosed Drives
Rating for the Durability of Helical and Herringbone Gears for Gearmotors
Rating for the Durability of Helical and Herringbone Gears for Shaft-Mounted Speed Reducers
Rating for the Surface Durability (Pitting) of Helical and Herringbone Gears for Rolling Mill Drives
Surface Durability (Pitting) Formulas for Straight Bevel and Zerol Bevel Gear Teeth
Information Sheet for Surface Durability (Pitting) of Spur, Helical, Herringbone and Bevel Gear Teeth
Surface Durability (Pitting) Formulas for Spiral Bevel Gear Teeth
Rating for the Surface Durability of Spiral Bevel Gears for Enclosed Drives
Rating for the Surface Durability of Spiral Bevel Gears for Gearmotors
Information Sheet — Gear Scoring Design Guide for Aerospace Spur and Helical Power Gears

STRENGTH

Rating the Strength of Spur Gear Teeth
Rating the Strength of Helical and Herringbone Gear Teeth
Rating for the Strength of Helical and Herringbone Gears for Enclosed Drives
Rating for the Strength of Helical and Herringbone Gears for Gearmotors
Rating for the Strength of Helical and Herringbone Gears for Shaft-Mounted Speed Reducers
Rating for the Strength of Helical and Herringbone Gears for Rolling Mill Drives
Rating the Strength of Straight Bevel and Zerol Bevel Gear Teeth
Rating the Strength of Spiral Bevel Gear Teeth
Rating for the Strength of Spiral Bevel Gears for Enclosed Drives
Rating for the Strength of Spiral Bevel Gears for Gearmotors
Information Sheet for Strength of Spur, Helical, Herringbone and Bevel Gear Teeth

INSPECTION

Surface Temper Inspection Process
Pin Measurement Tables for Involute Spur Gears
Inspection of Coarse-Pitch Cylindrical Worms and Wormgears
Information Sheet for Master Gears
Information Sheet for Data Gears Accuracy Specifications
Measuring Methods and Practices Manual for Control of Spur, Helical and Herringbone Gears
Measuring Methods and Practices Manual for Control of Bevel and Hypoid Gears

MATERIALS

Specification for General Industrial Gear Materials — Steel (Drawn, Rolled and Forged)
Cast Iron Gear Blanks
Cast Bronze Gear Blanks
Specification for Wormgear Bronze
Specification for Aluminum Bronze (Castings, Barstock and Forgings)
Specification for Manganese Bronze (Castings, Barstock and Forgings)
Nodular Iron Gear Materials
Specification for Cast Steel Gear Materials
Recommended Procedure for Carburized Industrial Gearing
Recommended Procedure of Nitriding, Materials and Process
Recommended Procedure for Induction Hardened Gears and Pinions
Recommended Procedure for Flame Hardening

LUBRICATION

Lubrication of Industrial Enclosed Gearing,
Specification — Lubrication of Industrial Gearing
Specification — Mild Extreme Pressure Lubricants for Industrial Enclosed Gearing
Information Sheet — Basic Information on Lubricating Oils
Information Sheet — Corrosion of Ferrous Metals, Its Causes, Prevention and Removal
Information Sheet — Data on Extreme Pressure Lubricants
Information Sheet — Lapping Procedures for Gears

90

BOLTING
Bolting (Allowable Tensile Stress) for Gear Drives

SHAFTING
Shafting — Allowable Torsional and Bending Stresses

BEARINGS
Bearings — Allowable Loads and Speeds

SPEEDS AND RATIOS
Output Speeds for Gearmotors
Ratios for Helical, Herringbone and Combination Spiral Bevel Gear Speed Reducers

MARKING
Marking for Enclosed Gear Drives
Information Sheet — Reducer Assembly Designations

SOUND TESTING
Specification for Measurement of Sound on High Speed Helical and Herringbone Gear Units

OPEN HELICAL AND HERRINGBONE GEARS
Design Practice for Helical and Herringbone Gears for Cylindrical Grinding Mills, Kilns and Dryers

OPEN BEVEL GEARS
Design Manual for Bevel Gears

OPEN WORMGEARING
Design of General Industrial Coarse-Pitch Cylindrical Wormgearing
Design of General Industrial Double-Enveloping Wormgears

MACHINE TOOL GEARING
Manual for Machine Tool Gearing

OPEN FINE-PITCH GEARS
Design for Fine-Pitch Wormgearing (USAS B6.9-1956)

GEAR CLASSIFICATION MANUALS
Gear Classification Manual

For additional information contact:

American Gear Manufacturers Association
1330 Massachusetts Avenue, N.W.
Washington, D.C. 20005

ENCLOSED SPUR GEARS
Design Procedure for Aircraft Engine and Power Take-Off Spur and Helical Gears

ENCLOSED HELICAL AND HERRINGBONE GEARS
Practice for Helical and Herringbone Gear Speed Reducers and Increasers
Practice for High Speed Helical and Herringbone Gear Units
Helical and Herringbone Gear Speed Reducers for Oilfield Pumping Units
Thermal Capacity of Helical, Herringbone and Combination-Spiral Bevel Speed Reducers
Practice for Helical and Herringbone Gearing for Oilfield Mud Pumps
Practice for In-Line Reducers and Increasers

ENCLOSED BEVEL GEARS
Practice for Speed Reducers and Increasers Employing Spiral Bevel Gearing
Design Procedure for Aircraft Engine and Power Take-Off Bevel Gears

ENCLOSED WORMGEARS
Practice for Single and Double-Reduction Cylindrical-Worm and Helical-Worm Speed Reducers
Practice for Single and Double-Reduction, Double-Enveloping Worm and Helical-Worm Speed Reducers
Practice for Worm Hollow Output Shaft Speed Reducers

GEARMOTORS
Practice for Gearmotors
Practice for Worm Gearmotors

ENCLOSED FINE-PITCH GEARS
Gearheads, Precision Control Motor (Servomotor)

SHAFT-MOUNTED REDUCERS
Practice for Helical, Herringbone and Spur Gear Shaft-Mounted Speed Reducers

COOLING TOWER DRIVES
Information Sheet — Selection and Maintenance of Gear Units for Water Cooling Tower Fan Drives

FLEXIBLE COUPLINGS
Nomenclature for Flexible Couplings
Bore and Keyseat Sizes for Flexible Couplings

February 1, 1969

Roster of
AGMA Member Companies

Abart Gear & Machine Co., 4830 West 16th St., Chicago, Ill. 60650
+ABA Tool & Die Co., Inc., 1395 Tolland Turnpike, Manchester, Conn. 06040
Aero Gear Machine & Tool Corp., 74 Industrial Ave., Little Ferry, N.J. 07643
Aircraft Gear Corp., 6633 West 65th St., Chicago, Ill. 60638
Ajax Flexible Coupling Co., Inc., Cor. English & Portage Stss., Westfield, N.Y. 14787
Alling-Lander Co., Inc., Div. of Garlock, Inc., 300 Alling Rd., Sodus, N.Y. 14551
Alten Foundry & Machine Works, Inc., 226 West Wheeling St., Lancaster, Ohio 43130
Amarillo Gear Co., P.O. Box 1789, 217 North Polk St., Amarillo, Tex. 79105
The American Pulley Co., Div. of Universal American Corp., 4200 Wissahickon Ave., Philadelphia, Pa. 19129
Ametek/Lamb Electric, Kent, Ohio 44240
Anadite Inc., Gear & Machining Div., 5000 U.S. Highway 81 South, P.O. Box 1990, Forth Worth, Tex. 76101
Arrow Gear Co., 2301 Curtiss St., Downers Grove, Ill. 60515
+Avco Lycoming Div., 550 South Main St., Stratford, Conn. 06497
Badger State Gear Co., Inc. 5135 North Thirty-Second St., Milwaukee, Wisc. 53209
+Barber-Colman Co., 1300 Rock St., Rockford, Ill. 61101
Beaver Gear Works, Inc., 5459 - 11th St., Rockford, Ill. 61105
Bedford Gear Div., The Scott & Fetzer Co., 7160 Krick Industrial Park, Cleveland, Ohio 44146
+The Bendix Corp., Industrial Metrology Div., 3621 South State Rd., Ann Arbor, Mich. 48106
+Blaw-Knox Co., Foundry & Mill Machinery Div., 300 Sixth Ave., Pittsburgh, Pa. 15222
+E. W. Bliss Co., Salem Plant, 530 South Ellsworth Ave., Salem, Ohio 44460
+The Boeing Co., Vertol Div., Boeing Center, P.O. Box 16858, Philadelphia, Pa. 19142
Commercial Airplane Div., Everett Branch, P.O. Box 3707, Seattle, Wash. 98124
Charles Bond Co., 1315-37 Windrim St., Philadelphia, Pa. 19141
Christiana Machine Company Div., Box 105, Christiana, Pa. 17509
Boston Gear Works Div., North American Rockwell Corp., 14 Hayward St., Quincy, Mass. 02171
Brad Foote Gear Works, Inc., 1309 South Cicero Ave., Cicero, Ill. 60650
Pittsburgh Gear Div., Neville Island, Pittsburgh, Pa. 15225
Braun Gear Co., 239 Richmond St., Brooklyn, N.Y. 11208
Browning Manufacturing Co., Box 687, Maysville, Ky. 41056
The Buehler Corp., 9000 Precision Drive, Indianapolis, Ind. 46236
Cabot Corp., Machinery Div., P.O. Box 1101, Pampa, Texas 79065
Camdale Precision, Inc., 15850 Common Rd., Rosevale, Mich. 48066
Capitol Gears, Inc., 349 North Hamline Ave., St. Paul, Minn. 55104
The Cincinnati Gear Co., Wooster Pike & Mariemont Ave., Cincinnati, Ohio 45227
Clipper Gear & Machine Co., 15301 East Twelve Mile Rd., Roseville, Mich. 48066
Cloyes Gear & Products, Inc., 17214 Roseland Rd., Cleveland, Ohio 44112
Cogmatic Machines, 3129 West Mill Rd., Milwaukee, Wisc. 53209
+Collins Radio Co., Cedar Rapids, Iowa 52402
+Colt Industries Inc., Pratt & Whitney Inc., Machine Tool Div., Charter Oak Blvd., West Hartford, Conn. 06101
Cotta Transmission Co., 2340 Eleventh St., Rockford, Ill. 61101
Charles E. Crofoot Gear Corp., South Easton, Mass. 02375
Curtiss-Wright Corp., Wood-Ridge Facility, Wood-Ridge, N.J. 07075
Caldwell Facility, Caldwell, N.J. 07006
Dearborn Tool & Manufacturing, Inc., 7239 West Wilson Ave., Chicago, Ill. 60631

De Laval-Holroyd, Inc., 121 First Ave., Trenton, N.J. 08607
De Laval Turbine Inc., Trenton, N.J. 08602
Diefendorf Gear Corp., P.O. Box 934, Syracuse, N.Y. 13201
Dominion Engineering Works Limited, First Ave., Lachine, Quebec, Canada
Dorris Co., 750 North Skinker Blvd., St. Louis, Mo. 63130
The Earle Gear & Machine Co., 4707 Stenton Ave., Philadelphia, Pa. 19144
*Eaton Ejes I.C.S.A., Subsidiary of Eaton Yale & Towne, Inc., Viamonte 1133 - 4° Piso, Buenos Aires, Argentina
Eaton Yale & Towne Inc., Cleveland Worm & Gear Div., 3249 East 80th St., Cleveland, Ohio 44104
General Products Group, 100 Erieview Plaza, Cleveland, Ohio 44114
Eaton Gear Div., 8th & South "O" Stss., Richmond, Ind. 47374
International Group, 100 Erieview Plaza, Cleveland, Ohio 44114
Fawick Airflex Div., 9919 Clinton Rd., Cleveland, Ohio 44111
+Engis Equipment Co., 8035 Austin Ave., Morton Grove, Ill. 60053
*Engranes y Maquinaria Arco, S.A., Calzada San Francisco No. 96, San Bartolo Naucalpan, Edo. de Mexico
Equitable Engineering Co., 2724 Normandy Rd., Royal Oak, Mich. 48073
Fairfield Manufacturing Co., Inc., U.S. 52 South, Lafayette, Ind. 47902
The Falk Corp., P.O. Box 492, 3001 West Canal St., Milwaukee, Wisc. 53201
Farrel Co., Div. of USM Corp., P.O. Box 193, 565 Blossom Rd., Rochester, N.Y. 14601
Federal Gear, Inc., 1734 East 47th St., Cleveland, Ohio 44103
The Fellows Gear Shaper Co., 78 River St., Springfield, Vt. 05156
Ferguson Gear Co., Gastonia, N.C. 28053
+FMC Corp., Ordnance Engineering Div., P.O. Box 367, San Jose, Calif. 95103
Forano Limited, 1600 St. Paul St., Plessisville, Quebec, Canada
+Ford Motor Co., Transmission & Chassis Div., P.O. Box 2097, Livonia, Mich. 48151
Franke Gear Works, Inc., 4401 Ravenswood Ave., Chicago, Ill. 60640
Franklin Electric Co., Inc., 400 East Spring St., Bluffton, Ind. 46714
Ganschow Gear Co., 12-20 North Morgan St., Chicago, Ill. 60607
+The Garrett Corp., AiResearch Manufacturing Div., 9851 Sepulveda Blvd., Los Angeles, Calif. 90009
AiResearch Manufacturing Div., 402 South 36th St., Phoenix, Ariz. 85034
Gear Specialties, Inc., 2635 West Medill Ave., Chicago, Ill. 60647
Gear Systems Div., USM Corp., 81 Bay State Rd., Wakefield, Mass. 01880
Geartronics Corp., 100 Chelmsford Rd., North Billerica, Mass. 01862
General Electric Co., Gear Business Section, Medium Steam Turbine, Generator & Gear Dept., 1100 Western Ave., West Lynn, Mass. 01905
Gear Motor Business Section, General Purpose Motor Dept., 845 East 25th St., Paterson, N.J. 07513
Home Laundry Dept., Louisville, Ky.
Motor & Generator Engineering Unit, Transportation Equipment Products Operation, Erie, Pa. 16501
Engineering Dept., Flight Propulsion Div., Cincinnati, Ohio 45215
+General Motors Corp., Technical Center, Research Laboratories, 12 Mile & Mound Roads, Warren, Mich. 48090
Allison Div., Indianapolis, Ind. 46206
Buick Motor Div., Flint, Mich. 48550
+Giddings & Lewis Machine Tool Co. Div., Fond du Lac, Wisc. 54935
+Gleason Works, 1000 University Ave., Rochester, N.Y. 14603
Hamilton Gear & Machine Co., Div. of Combined Engineered Products Ltd., 950-990 Dupont St., Toronto 4, Ontario, Canada
+Harnischfeger Corp., 4400 West National Ave., Milwaukee, Wisc. 53246
Holtzer-Cabot Corp., Janette Div., 125 Amory St., Boston, Mass. 02119
The Horsburgh & Scott Co., 5114 Hamilton Ave., Cleveland, Ohio 44114
Howard Industries, Div. of MSL Industries, Inc., 2420 18th St., Racine, Wisc. 53403

+Hughes Aircraft Co., Culver City, Calif. 90230

+Hughes Tool Co., Oil Tool Div., P.O. Box 2539, Houston, Tex. 77001

Aircraft Div., Centinela Ave. & Teale St., Culver City, Calif. 90230

Illinois Gear Div., Wallace-Murray Corp., 2108 North Natchez Ave., Chicago, Ill. 60635

Illinois Tool Works Inc., 2501 North Keeler Ave., Chicago, Ill. 60639

+Roy C. Ingersoll Research Center, Borg-Warner Corp., Wolf & Algonquin Rds., Des Plaines, Ill. 60018

+International Business Machines Corp., Systems Development Div., Endicott, N.Y. 13760

Systems Manufacturing Div., Endicott, N.Y. 13760

Systems Development Div., Raleigh, N.C. 27603

+International Harvester Co., General Office, 401 North Michigan Ave., Chicago, Ill. 60611

Engineering Research, 7 South 600 County Line Rd., Hinsdale, Ill. 60521

Solar Div., 2200 Pacific Highway, San Diego, Calif. 92112

Invincible Gear Co., 14938 Telegraph Rd., Detroit, Mich. 48239

Invo Spline, Inc., 2357 East Nine Mile Rd., Warren, Mich. 48090

Jackson Gear Co., Inc., P.O. Box 9508, Etna, Pittsburgh, Pa. 15223

D.O. James Gear Manufacturing Co., 1140 West Monroe St., Chicago, Ill. 60607

Johnson Gear & Manufacturing Co., Ltd., 8th & Parker Sts., Berkeley, Calif. 94710

Juall Gear Co., Inc., 1108 Goffle Rd., Hawthorne, N.J. 07506

+Kearney & Trecker Corp., 11000 Theodore Trecker Way, West Allis, Wisc. 53214

E.L. Klauber Machinery Co., Inc., 3221 Olive St., St. Louis, Mo. 63103

Koppers Co., Inc., Metal Products Div., P.O. Box 1696, Baltimore, Md. 21203

Lamont Gear Co., 4600 North Fairhill St., Philadelphia, Pa. 19140

+Landis Machine Co., A Teledyne Co., 5th & Church Sts., Waynesboro, Pa. 17268

+Lear Siegler, Inc., Instrument Div., 4141 Eastern Ave., S.E., Grand Rapids, Mich. 49508

Levy Industries Ltd., 207 Weston Rd., Toronto 9, Ontario, Canada

Canadian Acme Screw & Gear, Ltd., 207 Weston Rd., Toronto 9, Ontario, Canada

York Gears Ltd., 825 Caledonia Rd., Tornoto 19, Ontario, Canada

Link-Belt Div. of FMC Corp., Philadelphia Plant, 2045 West Hunting Park Ave., Philadelphia, Pa. 19140

Ewart Plant, 220 South Belmont Ave., Indianapolis, Ind. 46206

Link-Belt, Ltd., Box 173, Station "H", Toronto 13, Ontario, Canada

Litton Industries Inc., 9370 Santa Monica Blvd., Beverly Hills, Calif. 90213

The Louis Allis Div., 427 East Stewart St., Milwaukee, Wisc. 53201

Electra Motors Div., 1110 North Lemon St., Anaheim, Calif. 92803

Hewitt-Robins Div., Executive Offices, 666 Glenbrook Rd., Stamford, Conn. 06906

Hewitt-Robins Div., Gear Products Operations, 4545 South Western Blvd., Chicago, Ill. 60609

L.M. Gear Co., 23120 Gratiot Ave., East Detroit, Mich. 48021

Lufkin Foundry & Machine Co., P.O. Box 849, Lufkin, Tex. 75901

*Maag Gear-Wheel Co., Ltd., P.O. Box 8023, Zurich, Switzerland

Mantel Gear Works, Inc., 500 South Portland St., Seattle, Wash. 98108

Marples Gears, A Div. of Phillips Aviation Co., 1525 South Monterey Rd., South Pasadena, Calif. 91030

*Mecánica Falk, S.A. de C.V., Apartado 15016, México 16, D.F.

+Mechanical Technology Inc., 968 Albany Shaker Rd., Latham, N.Y. 12110

Michigan Tool Co., 7171 East McNichols Rd., Detroit, Mich. 48212

Micro Precision Gear & Machine Corp., 14300 Lorain Ave., Cleveland, Ohio 44111

Micron Gear Co., Inc., 210 Express St., Plainview, L.I., N.Y. 11803

Midland-Ross Corp., Waldron-Hartig Div., P.O. Box 791, New Brunswick, N.J. 08903

Milwaukee Gear Co., 5150 North Port Washington Rd., Milwaukee, Wisc. 53217

+Mixing Equipment Co., Inc., 135 Mount Read Blvd., Rochester, N.Y. 14611

+Morgan Construction Co., Worcester, Mass. 01605

Morse Chain, Div. of Borg-Warner Corp., Ithaca, N.Y. 14850

Eberhardt-Denver Plant, 4650 Steele St., Denver, Colo. 80216

National Broach & Machine Div., Lear Siegler, Inc., 5600 St. Jean Ave., Detroit, Mich. 48213

+National Tool Co., Div. of National Cleveland Corp., 11200 Madison Ave., Cleveland, Ohio 44102

+National Twist Drill & Tool Co., Rochester, Mich. 48063

New Jersey Gear & Manufacturing Co., Inc., 1470 Chestnut Ave., Hillside, N.J. 07025

Nixon Gear & Machine Co., Inc., P.O. Box 187, Colvin Station, 185 Ainsley Drive, Syracuse, N.Y. 13205

+Norton Co., Machine Tool Div., G&E Section, Worcester, Mass. 01606

O'Brien Gear & Machine Co., P.O. Box D, 2396 Skokie Valley Rd., Highland Park, Ill. 60035

Ohio Gear Div. of Towmotor Corp., 1333 East 179th St., Cleveland, Ohio 44110

Oilwell Div., U.S. Steel Corp., P.O. Box 308, Garland, Tex. 75040

Box 1107, Oil City, Pa. 16301

Oliver Gear & Machine Co., Inc., 1114-1120 Niagara St., Buffalo, N.Y. 14213

+Otis Elevator Co., 260 Eleventh Ave., New York, N.Y. 10001

44 Wells Ave., Yonkers, N.Y. 10701

Overton Gear & Tool Corp., 530 Westgate Drive, Addison, Ill. 60101

Pennsylvania Gear, Inc., Sunbury, Pa. 17801

Perkins Machine & Gear Co., Circuit Ave., West Springfield, Mass. 01089

Philadelphia Gear Corp., King of Prussia, Pa. 19406

PIC Design Corp., 477 Atlantic Ave., East Rockaway, N.Y. 11518

Precision Gear Co., Inc., P.O. Box 309, 618 Washington St., Walpole, Mass. 02081

Precision Molded Gearing Corp., Dean St., Norwood, Mass. 02062

Process Gear Co., Inc., 3313 West Newport Ave., Chicago, Ill. 60618

Progressive Engineering Co., 2010 East Main St., Richmond, Va. 23223

Quaker City Gear Works, Inc., Red Lion Rd. & Philmont Ave., Huntingdon Valley, Pa. 19006

Radio Corp. of America, Defense Electronic Products, Moorestown, N.J. 08057

Randolph Manufacturing Co., 1110 North Ave. T, P.O. Box 5306, Lubbock, Tex. 79417

Rawling Gear Works, Inc., 890 Hartford Pike (Route 20), Shrewsbury, Mass. 01545

+Raytheon Co., Bedford Laboratories, Hartwell Rd., Bedford, Mass. 01730

Reef Industries Div., Reef-Baker Corp., 21500 Gratiot Ave., East Detroit, Mich. 48021

Reliance Electric Co., 24701 Euclid Ave., Cleveland, Ohio 44117

Research, Development, Engineering; 24800 Tungsten Rd.; Cleveland, Ohio 44117

Dodge Manufacturing Div., 500 South Union St., Mishawaka, Indiana 46544

Master Electric Div., 3300 Tenth St., Columbus, Ind. 47201

Rex Chainbelt Inc., Thomas Coupling Div., P.O. Box 549, Warren, Pa. 16365

Riley Gear Corp., Div. Associated Oil & Gas Co., 61 Felton St., North Tonawanda, N.Y. 14120

Rochester Bevel Gear Co., Inc., 20 Saginaw Drive, Rochester, N.Y. 14623

Rochester Gear Service, Inc., 419 Cox Bldg., 36 St. Paul St., Rochester, N.Y. 14604

+Rocketdyne Div., North American Rockwell Corp., 6633 Canoga Ave., Canoga Park, Calif. 91304

Rogers & Oling, Inc., 2670 East Walnut St., Pasadena, Calif. 91107

St. Louis Gear Co., Inc., P.O. Box 8, Highway 218, Keokuk, Iowa 52632

Schafer Gear Works, Inc., 814-820 South Main St., South Bend, Ind. 46623

*SECIM, 107 Blvd. de la Mission Marchand, 92 Courbevoie, France

Sewall Gear Manufacturing Company, 705 Raymond Ave., St. Paul, Minn. 55114

Sier-Bath Gear Co., Inc., 9252 Kennedy Blvd., North Bergen, N.J. 07047

The Simonds Gear & Manufacturing Co., 2501 Liberty Ave., Pittsburgh, Pa. 15222

Skidmore Gear Co., 17045 Euclid Ave., Cleveland, Ohio 44112

Smallwood & Son Machine Co., 3657 East Kiest Blvd., P.O. Box 9365, Dallas, Tex. 75215

+F. L. Smidth & Co., Inc., 1270 Avenue of the Americas, New York, N.Y. 10020

Gear Manufacturing Plant, Lebanon, New Jersey 08833

The Snow-Nabstedt Gear Corp., 55 Defco Park Rd., Defco Industrial Park, P.O. Box 176, North Haven, Conn. 06473
SPECO Div., Kelsey-Hayes Co., 1205 West Columbia St., Springfield, Ohio 45501
Stahl Gear & Machine Co., 3901 Hamilton Ave., Cleveland, Ohio 44114
Standard Steel Specialty Co., P.O. Box 20, Beaver Falls, Pa. 15010
Sterling Electric Motors, Inc., A Subsidiary of the Lionel Corp., 5401 Telegraph Rd., Los Angeles, Calif. 90022
Sterling Instrument, Div. of Designatronics, Inc., 76 East Second St., Mineola, N.Y. 11501
+Sundstrand Aviation Div., Sundstrand Corp., 4747 Harrison Ave., Rockford, Ill. 61101
Superite Gear & Instrument Corp., 140 Oak Drive, Syosset, L.I., N.Y. 11791
Taylor & Gaskin, Inc., Palmer-Bee Div., 6440 Mack Ave., Detroit, Mich. 48201
The Terry Steam Turbine Co., P.O. Box 1200, Hartford, Conn. 06101
The Tool Steel Gear & Pinion Co., Elmwood Place, Cincinnati, Ohio 45216
Tool Steel Products Sales Corp., 7711 Camargo Rd., Cincinnati, Ohio 45243
*Tsubakimoto-Morse Co., Ltd., 620 Tsurumicho, Joto-ku, Osaka, Japan
+United Engineering & Foundry Co., 948 Fort Duquesne Blvd., Pittsburgh, Pa. 15222
U.S. Electrical Motors Div., Emerson Electric Co., 200 East Slauson Ave., Los Angeles, Calif. 90054
Old Gate Lane, Milford, Conn. 06460
+United States Steel Corp., Corporate Engineering Offices, 525 William Penn Place, Pittsburgh, Pa. 15230
+UTD Corp., Union-Card Div., 134 Chestnut Hill Ave., Athol, Mass. 01331
Vancouver Gear Works Ltd., 975 Vernon Drive, Vancouver 6, B.C., Canada
+Verson Allsteel Press Co., 1355 East Ninety-Third St., Chicago, Ill. 60619
The Walter Machine Co., Inc., 84-98 Cambridge Ave., Jersey City, N.J. 07307
+The Warner & Swasey Co., 5701 Carnegie Ave., Cleveland, Ohio 44103

Western Gear Corp., Executive Offices, P.O. Box 182, Lynwood, Calif. 90262
Precision Products Div., P.O. Box 190, Lynwood, Calif. 90262
Systems Management Div., P.O. Box 333, Lynwood, Calif. 90262
Heavy Machinery Div., Everett, Wash. 98201
Graphic Arts Div., P.O. Box 190, Lynwood, Calif. 90262
Electro Products Div., 75 West Green St., Pasadena, Calif. 91101
Industrial Products Div., P.O. Box 126, Belmont, Calif. 94003
Southwestern Div., P.O. Box 4008, Houston, Tex. 77014
Westinghouse Electric Corp., Motor & Gearing Div., P.O. Box 225, Buffalo, N.Y. 14240
Marine Mechanical Dept., Sunnyvale, Calif. 94088
Small Steam & Gas Turbine Div., Lester, Pa. 19113
Elevator Div., Jersey City, N.J. 07304
Defense & Space Center, P.O. Box 746, Baltimore, Md. 21203
+Wheelabrator Corp., Mishawaka, Ind. 46544
Winsmith, Div. of UMC Industries, Inc., Springville, Erie County, N.Y. 14141
Worcester Gear Works, Inc., 18 Grafton St., Worcester, Mass. 01604
Worth Harmes Gear Co., Inc., 2970 North Weil St., Milwaukee, Wisc. 53212
Worthington Corp., Turbine Div., Wellsville, N.Y. 14895
Air Conditioning Div., 14 Fourth Ave., East Orange, N.J. 07017
X L Gears, Inc., 69 Prospect St., Newark, N.J. 07105
Zurn Industries, Inc., Mechancial Drives Div., Erie, Pa. 16512

+Technical Member
*International Member